Fat-Burning Foods

Over 100 different slimming recipes
to suit everyone's tastes

Abbreviations

approx. = approximately
CH   = carbohydrate(s)
cm   = centimetre(s)
F   = fat
g   = gram(s)
kcal   = kilocalory(-ies)
kg   = kilogram(s)
kJ   = kilojoule(s)
l   = litre(s)
ml   = millilitre(s)
mm   = millimetre(s)
NFC   = not from concentrate
P   = protein
tbsp   = tablespoon(s)
tsp   = teaspoon(s)

Measurements

1 tsp   = 5 ml
1 tbsp   = 10 ml
1 cup   = 150 ml
1 litre   = 1000 ml
½ litre   = 500 ml
¼ litre   = 250 ml
⅛ litre   = 125 ml

Fat-Burning Foods

Over 100 different slimming recipes
to suit everyone's tastes

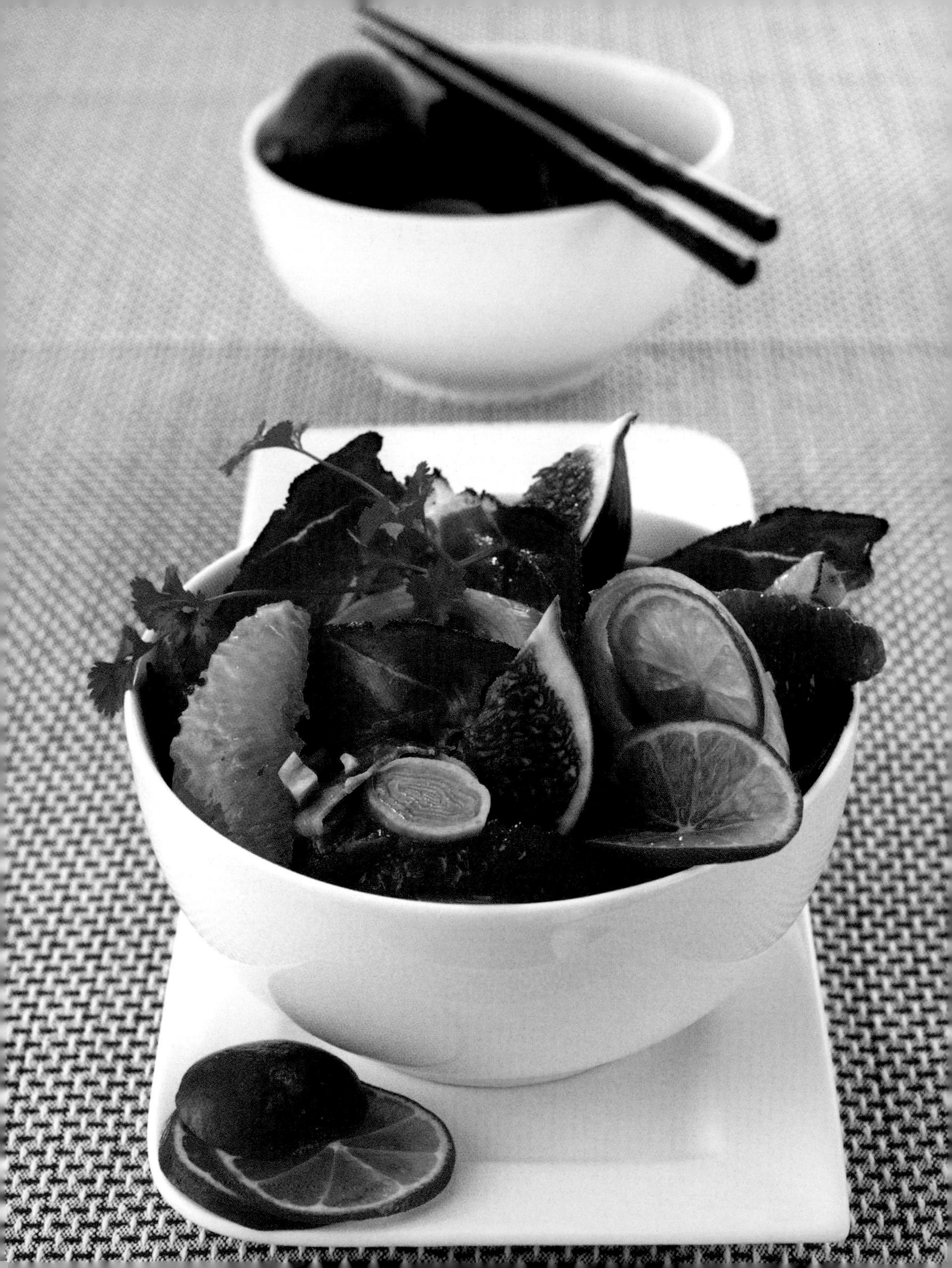

Foreword

The Greek word *diaita*, from which we get the word "diet", simply means "way of life". Unfortunately, in the modern world dieting is very often identified with abstinence, fasting, suffering and other negative features. It should really stand for eating in a sensible way that allows you to reach and maintain a body weight at which you feel good – your own, very personal, feel-good body weight.

Think of diet in the original meaning of *diaita* as a way of life, specifically as a way of life that helps you to feel fit, satisfied and contented. You can achieve all this if you eat fat-burning foods, because they act directly on the metabolism, speeding it up and ensuring that fats are burned at a high rate. Our book shows you how it works. The detailed introduction tells you which fat-burning foods are right for you and the best ways to combine them, and this is followed by over 100 very varied recipes for use every day.

Contents

Introduction

Shedding the pounds permanently

Perhaps you have already tried a few diets, given up tasty treats for days or weeks at a time and put up with a rumbling tummy for the reward of seeing the needle on the scales move less and less far round. It was worth all the torture – wasn't it?

But how often has it happened that shortly after dieting your scales have shown more than they did before?

This is the result of the notorious yo-yo effect. When the body suddenly gets less "fodder", it breaks down fatty deposits in the body. Great, you're losing weight! But at the same time, the lack of nourishment gives the body a signal to switch to the pilot light. Unfortunately this fuel-saving mechanism is not immediately switched back to normal operation when you're eating as usual again. Everything you now put into your body is very efficiently converted. You can't help putting on weight. The next diet awaits.

You won't get permanently slim by avoiding calories. On the contrary, you have to eat in order to lose weight! You have to give your body enough to prevent it from going into deficiency mode and changing the way it metabolises energy. Give your body what it needs, specifically in the form of fat-burning foods, which contain natural substances that will gradually burn up your fat reserves.

Eat yourself slim with fat-burning foods

What is fat-burning?

You have decided to deal with your superfluous pounds by burning up the fat. Congratulations! You have selected an effective method for reaching your desired weight and, even more importantly, being able to maintain it in the long term without fasting.

The term "fat-burning" refers to what you want to achieve: burning up body fat in order to be slimmer and feel fitter. And you can achieve this with a whole series of foods that have fat-burning properties. This does not mean that you are only allowed to eat a few particular foods, as is the case with many diets. Don't worry, you don't have to eat almost nothing but pineapple for weeks on end or live on cabbage soup from morning till night. You wouldn't be able to stand it for long and it would even make you ill in the long run. Your diet can be as rich and varied as usual – perhaps even more varied, as you may come across some foods that you have not previously paid much attention to and eat them in preference to other things that won't play such a big part in your meals in future.

The pounds melt away with fat-burning foods

How do fat-burning foods work?

One of the key principles of fat-burning foods is their influence on glucose levels in the blood. Glucose not only supplies energy but also represents a kind of sugar-level indicator that shows how the body's supply of nutrients is looking.

A normal level is about one gram of sugar in a litre of blood. If this level rises or falls due to eating more or less food, various processes are set in motion in the body, resulting in the storing or breakdown of nutrients.

Fat-burning foods, which contain carbohydrates that break down slowly, ensure that the level never falls low enough to cause cravings. You feel full for longer and eat less. However, at the same time these foods actively attack the fat pads, because the breakdown of carbohydrates requires energy. The more complex their construction, the more energy the body has to use in order to retain glucose.

But the body does not live on carbohydrates alone. Protein and – yes, really – even fat are also nutrients the body needs, as well as vitamins, minerals, trace elements and hormones. In all these cases, fat-burning foods contain substances that are death to fatty deposits while providing for the body in the best possible way.

Choose fresh foods for preference

Individual fat-burning agents

Nutrition experts today base their ideas on the assumption that the insulin level is the crucial, possibly the only, cause of obesity. But you don't have to start monitoring your insulin level now, you only need to look behind the scenes in order to understand what happens to the food inside the body and how you can influence it through your diet.

Before that, one more important piece of advice: banish convenience foods from your diet wherever you can. Ready meals contain barely enough vitamins, minerals and trace elements and consist mainly of "dead" nutrients. Seventy per cent of what you eat should consist of natural foods. Then your body will forgive you for the remaining thirty per cent of unhealthy convenience foods, which are almost always fattening.

Simple and complex carbohydrates – a big difference

The insulin level is affected by sugar, so looking at your own sugar consumption is the key factor in successful weight loss. However, all carbohydrates are not the same.

"Bad" sugars

The types of sugar that make our lives sweeter come as single or double sugars. Saccharose, our ordinary household sugar, is a double sugar consisting of one molecule of fructose and one molecule of glucose. When you eat something sweetened with sugar, this sugar is rapidly split into two parts in the gut; the glucose is immediately absorbed into the blood and has already given your body a powerful energy boost.

As the body is anxious to keep the level of glucose in the blood stable at all times, this high quantity of sugar must be removed from the blood quickly and stored in the places provided for it, so the pancreas releases the appropriate amount of the hormone insulin to control glucose storage and sends satiation signals to the brain. If the glucose stores in the liver and muscles are full, glucose is converted into fat and stored around the tummy, hips and

There are sugar traps lurking everywhere, also in breakfast

Fresh fruit gives you energy and stimulates the metabolism

all the other places we find it so hard to lose it from. Because the glucose is removed from the blood so quickly by large quantities of insulin, the glucose level quickly falls again. A real craving soon returns and in the worst case you reach for the sweets again and the drama continues to unfold.

"Good" sugars

However, our body needs glucose to supply energy, as the brain and muscles can't work without it. We have to provide it with glucose – but how do we do so, if glucose makes you fat? Quite simply, it has to be ingested in a form in which it is released slowly and continuously into the blood. This is done by complex carbohydrates, multiple sugars, which are made up of many sugar molecules and therefore break down slowly and continuously.

The insulin level rises equally slowly, just fast enough to transport the glucose gradually to the cells.

Glucagon – the fat-burning hormone

Now the hormone glucagon, an insulin antagonist, also gets a chance. It is released by the pancreas as soon as a certain proportion of the sugar has been broken down in the blood and the blood-sugar level has consequently fallen below a particular value. Firstly glucagon slows down the activity of insulin and secondly it also promotes the release of fat from the fat cells so that it can be converted into sugar if needed.

Roughage – the insulin retardant

Single and double sugars are fattening, so in principle you should treat all sweeteners like a seasoning and not as something to fill you up.

Luckily things are different where fruit is concerned. In this case roughage slows the rate at which the fructose contained in the fruit is absorbed into the blood from the gut, so the insulin level cannot shoot up too high. The same also happens with wholegrain products. Their higher proportion of roughage delays the slow breakdown of the complex carbohydrate chain still further. Another advantage is that you feel full for a long time, because it takes three hours for the sugar to disperse in the blood.

The glycaemic index

The glycaemic index (GI) is the accepted way of measuring the increase in blood sugar caused by a foodstuff. On a scale of 1 to 110, all foods with an index number above 55 are bad for the figure. These are foods containing sugar and also highly processed products containing carbohydrates, which no longer supply any roughage that could delay the absorption of glucose into the blood.

Whole grain bread slows down insulin production

Fat does not necessarily make you fat

First the bad news: too much fat really does make you fat, because the body stores every fat calorie it doesn't need in the fat cells for emergencies. So reducing fat is definitely a good idea but doing without it completely is not. As with carbohydrates, there are big differences between fats. Many fats are actually essential for the body – even for losing weight.

Avocados contain many good fats

"Good" fats

Good fats include the unsaturated fatty acids, which the body cannot produce for itself. They are found mainly in vegetable foodstuffs. These fatty acids are vitally important. Among

Single unsaturated fatty acids	Double unsaturated fatty acids	Polyunsaturated fatty acids	Saturated fatty acids
Olive oil	Soya oil	Herrings	Coconut butter
Groundnut oil	Corn oil	Salmon	Butter
Rapeseed oil	Sunflower oil	Tuna	Clarified butter
		Mackerel	Cheese
		Linseed oil	Dairy products
		Walnut oil	Meat and sausages
			Many ready meals

other things, they make hormones that ensure digestion functions smoothly and the bile salts that are indispensable for the digestion of fat. Last but not least, if you fulfil your need for fat with "good" unsaturated fats, you will not hunger for unhealthy saturated fatty acids that only make you fat and offer the body nothing more.

"Bad" fats

It is best to avoid saturated fatty acids of the kind mainly found in animal products such as meat, sausages, cheese, butter and cream, as they go straight to the fat deposits. However, there are also "good" fats to be found among the animal fats, like the conjugated linoleic acid in yoghurt and fish. It helps to prevent cancer and allergies and even keeps you slim. In this connection you should definitely not switch to low-fat products. You should steer well clear of foods containing hydrogenated fats that do not occur naturally and are therefore only to be found in ready-made products, because the many trans fatty acids in them may even cause cancer and increase the risk of heart attacks.

A bad combination: fat and carbohydrates

Mostly you don't eat only fats or only carbohydrates but combine both in one meal. However, a nice roast with filling accompaniments of carbohydrates can have dire consequences, as the carbohydrate-rich accompaniment quickly sends the insulin level shooting up. The insulin pounces on the fat from the roast and instantly stores the fat molecules in the fat cells, so a meal of this kind goes straight to the hips. However, if you

Do not treat yourself to this combination too often

choose an accompaniment containing carbohydrates that raise the blood sugar slowly and therefore cause only a little insulin to be released, the fat in the muscle cells can be converted into energy.

Protein

Protein is one of the most important building materials in the body. Muscles, nerves, organs, immune system and hair: everything is made up of 22 amino acids, the building blocks of protein.

Protein makes you slim
Protein is also an indispensable nutrient if you want to get slim, because breaking down protein requires energy, which comes from the fat cells – one kilocalorie for four kilocalories of protein, to be precise. Wonderful, you think, then I only have to eat nothing but protein and I will get slim automatically. And this is true, but unfortunately the slimming effect is deceptive, because if you eat mainly protein, your body switches to an alternative metabolic programme, ketosis. Ketone bodies are produced

and the body tries to get rid of them by excreting large amounts of water. This looks good on the scales but is also good for the fat pads, which continue to thrive. This is yet another demonstration of the fact that extreme diets with an unnatural nutrient content are not healthy and do not lead to lasting success.

Combining protein
So how can we make use of the slimming properties of protein? Once again it is by combining different foodstuffs with effects that complement one another. If you eat foods with "good" carbohydrates which, as a rule, are also foods which contain many important vitamins, minerals and trace elements, they immediately supply all the elements the body needs in order to break down protein and the protein can be broken down in the normal way with the help of the fat cells.

Not all protein is the same

You already have an inkling: there are differences between proteins as well. Essentially, there is a distinction between animal and vegetable protein. Just as animals are more like humans than plants, their protein is more like human protein and more valuable as nourishment. Unfortunately, in most cases animal protein comes with rather unhealthy fat, while foods with vegetable protein provide healthy roughage. That is why it is better to eat vegetable rather than animal proteins and to ensure that foods with animal protein do not have much fat in them. You can raise the low utilisation rate by combining various sources of protein with complementary amino acid patterns – protein structures – for instance egg with potatoes, beans with sweetcorn and milk with wholegrain flour.

Dairy products provide the body with a lot of protein

Redcurrants contain a lot of vitamin C

Vitamins, minerals and trace elements

Vitamins, minerals and trace elements are components of hormones, enzymes, the immune system and blood corpuscles, and control the metabolism. This means, of course, that they are important regulating factors in the storing and breakdown of fat. The following are the most important.

Vitamin C plays a key role in the metabolism of fat. It helps in the production of the hormones noradrenaline and carnitine, which promote the breakdown of fat.

Magnesium deficiency makes itself known in a very unpleasant way through muscle cramps. As soon as you become aware of this you should pay attention to your magnesium intake, as this mineral is important for fat-burning. It regulates the provision of oxygen to the cells and this in turn affects fat-burning.

In addition to the role it plays in building strong bones, **calcium** also has slimming effects. It supports the digestive enzymes and also dehydrates the body.

Chromium plays a part in glucose metabolism and in burning protein and fat.

Iodine is the key element in thyroxin. If the thyroid gland is not supplied with the right amount of iodine, it cannot produce sufficient hormones and all systems run at a snail's pace – including the breakdown of fat.

Hormones

In addition to insulin and glucagon, there are other metabolic messenger substances that determine whether fat is deposited on the hips.

The **growth hormone** is active at night. A good hour after falling asleep it is pumped into the blood from the pituitary gland. From there it goes into the fatty tissue, where it mobilises fat. It is formed from the two amino acids arginine and lysine.

Carnitine is the hormone that transports fat from the blood into the cells, where it is then converted into energy. Protein deficiency can quickly lead to carnitine deficiency.

Similar to adrenaline, **noradrenaline** is a hormone that makes a lot of energy available in times of stress, and it gets this energy from the fat cells. However, long-term stress has the opposite effect, because the hormones need to be supplied with sweet things.

The most important fat-burning foods

Fruit

Fruit is healthy, there is nothing new about that. But do those sweet little fruits also make you slim? Most of them do, because the glucose uptake is slowed down by roughage. But all the same, bear in mind that with very sweet fruits the roughage cannot entirely compensate for the high proportion of sugar.

The pectin contained in **apples** regulates the digestion, slows down the absorption of glucose and makes you feel full. Apples contain a lot of vitamin C, as well as potassium and magnesium.

The pantothenic acid contained in **apricots** makes them fat-burners, as it stimulates the breakdown of fat. The beta-carotene content protects the skin and makes it look fresh.

Avocados contain good unsaturated fatty acids as well as the carbohydrate mannoheptulose, a substance that actively lowers blood sugar.

Apricots are thought to be super-fat-burning

Unripe (!) bananas contain a special fat-killer known as resistant starch.

Citrus fruits are fat-burners par excellence, as their many flavonoids make the effect of their vitamin C content about twenty times stronger. Bitter substances in grapefruit reduce the appetite.

Currants are the stars of fat-burning, because they combine many positive substances: a large amount of vitamin C, as well as potassium, pantothenic acid, magnesium and manganese.

Dried fruit is a good alternative when you have a craving for something sweet. Fruits like apricots and plums with a lower proportion of sugar and a higher proportion of roughage keep the insulin level low, whereas sweeter types like raisins and dates have a high glycaemic index.

Kiwis have a high vitamin C content, which helps to break down fat, as well as calcium, potassium and iron.

The flesh of **mangos** aids digestion and the antioxidant effect of their vitamins and high beta-carotene content protect the cells.

Papayas supply many enzymes, which break down proteins and make them easier to digest.

Pears have a diuretic effect, thanks to their high potassium content. The trace element boron raises the testosterone level, which is also good for women as it makes people active.

Kiwis are real vitamin C bombs

Although **pineapple** has a high glycaemic index, it contains the enzyme bromelain, which makes protein easier to digest, as well as many minerals.

Plums have a purgative effect, especially when dried, because of their high roughage content.

Strawberries have the highest manganese content of any fruit, so they have a positive effect on thyroid function, and the potassium they contain is diuretic.

Vegetables

Vegetables contain many substances we need – even for weight loss: roughage, essential oils, chlorophyll, secondary plant substances, vitamins, minerals and trace elements. Try to eat a kilo a day, in main meals, juice and salads and to nibble between meals.

The agent cynarin, which is contained in **artichokes**, helps the liver with detoxifying and stimulates the digestion.

Asparagus, which contains a lot of folic acid, is virtually calorie-free and flushes superfluous water out of the body.

Cabbage contains almost no calories and its firm consistency requires plenty of chewing, which makes you feel full. It has plenty of vitamin C for slimming and its high potassium content has a diuretic effect.

Carrots, or their pectins, quickly make you feel full. They are best eaten raw, as when cooked they have a high glycaemic index.

The bitter substances, hormones and essential oils of **celeriac** stimulate the digestion.

Chicory has virtually no calories and contains the bitter substance intybin, which stimulates the digestion and the metabolism. Chicory contains vitamin C, calcium, magnesium, iron and potassium.

Vegetables provide many vital substances. Dig in!

Leeks contain not only plenty of roughage but also calcium, vitamin C, iron and magnesium.

Mooli and **radishes** have heaps of calcium, potassium, vitamin C and trace elements. Their essential oils stimulate the digestion.

Mushrooms have a low glycaemic index but a high protein content. Oyster mushroom also contain the substance chitosan, which can bind fats very well and thus prevent their uptake.

Onions are a true miracle food, as their potassium, calcium, iron, iodine, selenium and essential oils mean they can lower blood-sugar levels, break down fat, detoxify and calm the nerves.

Pulses contain a lot of roughage and vegetable protein. Beans contain glucokinins which, like insulin, lower the blood-sugar level.

Seaweeds are great providers of roughage and vitamins and contain a lot of iodine, which stimulates the metabolism via the thyroid gland.

Tomatoes contain a lot of potassium, which has a diuretic effect.

Cereals

The high roughage content of **wholegrain (rye) bread, rye sourdough bread** and **pumpernickel** means that insulin levels rise only moderately compared with bread made from wheat or mixed flour. If possible, eat them without fat. Low-fat quark is a tasty alternative to butter.

Oat flakes contain magnesium, iron and B vitamins. This makes them good food for the nerves.

Linseed belongs in the healthy kitchen

The ideal breakfast: oat flakes

The roughage in **linseed** strengthens the intestinal mucous membrane, has a purgative effect and saves insulin.

Milk and dairy products

The natural fat content of **milk, yoghurt** and other **dairy products** means they are also non-fattening, because their conjugated linoleic acid keeps you slim. They also contain the fat-burners calcium, magnesium and taurine.

Whey, kefir and buttermilk are low-calorie protein providers.

Low-fat cheese offers plenty of calcium and little fat. Cottage cheese and mozzarella are rich in satiating proteins and have little fat. The cheese with the lowest fat content is the German curd cheese Harzer Käse. The vitamin B 12 it contains stimulates the metabolism. It is better not to eat higher-fat cheeses with bread, as this combination of protein and carbohydrate makes you fat.

Fish and seafood

Fish should be on the menu once or twice a week, and not only because it is a great fat-burner. Its protein stimulates fat-burning and it provides an amino acid from which the body produces the slimming hormones

Fish is a winner, with plenty of protein, iodine and an amino acid

Crustaceans such as prawns contain hardly any fat

Salmon is particularly rich in omega-3 fatty acids, **sardines** have a high protein content and **mackerel** contain a lot of tyrosine.

Crustaceans and shellfish provide large amounts of zinc.

Meat

The high protein and iron content make meat a good fat-burner, but only if you keep your eye on the fat content. Beef, mutton and pork in particular may have a high fat content. White meats such as poultry and veal are better, because they contain less fat.

dopamine and noradrenaline. The high iron content stimulates the thyroid gland.

Cod is particularly low in fat; **squid** is almost fat-free.

Fillet of veal is particularly low in fat. Boiled ham with the fat cut off, turkey ham and smoked rolled ham are low-fat variations for cold, sliced meats. Turkey breast has very valuable protein and, like **boiled ham,** stimulates fat-burning in the body.

Corned Beef is filling and suppresses hunger.

Ox liver is rich in vitamins, which promote optimum burning of nutrients.

Avoid sausages, as they contain a lot of saturated fats. And keep away from anything fried in breadcrumbs or batter, which will have a high glycaemic index because they are prepared with white flour.

Drinks

You mustn't underestimate the effect of drinks on body-weight. Cola, sweet soft drinks and sweetened fruit juices have a high sugar content and usually have no nutrients of any value. Beer has the highest glycaemic index because of the maltose. These drinks should be taboo.

Water is the number one thirst-quencher for slimming. Drunk on an empty stomach it will still the pangs of hunger and stimulate the metabolism. You can heighten this effect with fresh lemon juice with plenty of fleshy bits. Beware of mineral water with a high magnesium content.

Coffee enhances fat-burning because it increases energy requirements.

Green tea contains bitter substances that make you feel full and help you lose weight, as well as many minerals.

Black tea contains more chromium than almost any other foodstuff.

Mate tea stimulates the metabolism and makes you feel full.

Freshly squeezed **fruit and vegetable juices**, without added sugar, of course, give your body a vitamin, mineral and trace element boost as well as valuable secondary plant substances.

Green tea invigorates body and mind

Water is the elixir of life and keeps you slim

Herbs and spices

Herbs and spices can be good **fat-burners**:

Chilli burns calories, because the capsaicin gets energy consumption going.

Cinnamon ensures that you use less insulin and so feel less hungry.

Sage aids the digestion of fat.

Chives are a diuretic.

Foods with a high glycaemic index (GI)

These foodstuffs encourage the production of the hormone insulin and consequently increase the risk of putting on weight. You should therefore minimise your consumption of all foods with a GI of over 55 and be sure not to combine them with fatty foods.

Fruit
Dates, dried 105
Banana 70
Watermelon 70
Honeydew melon 65
Raisins... 65
Pineapple 65
Figs, dried 60
Banana, ripe 60
Papaya... 58
Tinned fruit 55

Vegetables
Parsnips... 95
Carrots, boiled............................. 85
Pumpkin... 75
Beetroot 65

Potatoes
Roast potatoes............................. 95
Chips... 90
Baked potatoes............................. 85
Gnocchi... 70
Mashed potato 70
Boiled potatoes............................. 70
Potatoes boiled in their skins 60
Sweet potato 60

Rice and noodles
Risotto rice................................... 113
Instant rice................................... 85
Egg noodles 70
White rice...................................... 70

Bread
Pretzel... 85
Hamburger rolls.......................... 85
White bread................................... 85
Toasting loaf 75
Wholegrain wheat bread............. 65
Mixed-grain bread....................... 65

Cereal products
Popcorn.. 85
Cornflakes 85
Puffed rice 85
Polenta... 70
Sweetened muesli 70
Couscous....................................... 65

Cakes and pastries
Doughnuts..................................... 76
Yeast pastries 72
Croissants...................................... 70
Muffins 62

Sweets and snacks

Grape sugar	100
Potato crisps	98
Savoury nibbles	85
Gummibears	80
Ice cream with wafer	80
Chocolate bar	70
Milk chocolate	70
Jam/jelly	65
Butter biscuits	55

Drinks

Beer	110
Fruit juice, sweetened	90
Isotonic drinks	80
Soft drinks	70
Cola drinks	70

Foods with a low glycaemic index (GI)

Meat

Turkey breast	1
Veal fillet or schnitzel	1

Lentils	30
Red beans	40
Chick peas	40

Bread and cereals

Wild rice	35
Wholemeal noodles	35
Pumpernickel	40
Oat flakes	45
Parboiled rice	50
Wholegrain or bran loaf	50

Fruit

Grapefruit	25
Apricots	30
Figs	35
Oranges	40
Apples	40
Pears	40
Freshly squeezed fruit juice, unsweetened	40

Vegetables and pulses

Broccoli	15
Red cabbage	15
Aubergines	15
Courgettes	15
Soya beans	15
Carrots (raw)	30

Dairy products

Milk	30
Whole-milk products	10–30

Fat-burning and ...

If you stick to the fat-burning rules in your diet, you are already providing your body with a very good basis for reducing fat in the long term. However, as with all diets, simply changing your eating habits is unfortunately only the first step. You have to take exercise in order to lose weight and stay slim, otherwise you will reduce muscle mass, and the fat-burners are located in the muscles. You must ensure your body has rest and activity regularly and in the correct proportions. Then that is all you need to pay attention to in order to lead a better, easier and happier life.

Make sure you exercise

... exercise

First the good news. You don't have to, indeed you shouldn't, work yourself into a sweat in order to lose weight. Of course you have to take exercise, but in moderation and most of all for enjoyment. The fact is that with strenuous physical effort, such as a tennis match, a sprint or weightlifting, you certainly exert yourself and work up a sweat, but it makes no difference to your fat pads, because exercising too strenuously results in oxygen deficiency in the body, which then obtains its energy from carbohydrates instead of from fat.

So what's the bad news? There isn't any, unless you are a real couch potato who finds even walking from the sofa to the fridge a strain. You aren't in that bad a state? Then you shouldn't find it difficult to schedule in 30 minutes a day for fitness, when you take some physical exercise. It doesn't have to be sport; climbing stairs, housework or gardening can help to make the pounds melt away. And make sure it isn't too

Sufficient sleep stimulates fat breakdown

exhausting, as you must stay below the so-called training pulse rate, because only then will your body burn fat and it will do so during rest periods as well. Incidentally, the insulin level will also fall. Types of physical activity that allow you to do this without too much effort are walking, jogging, cycling and skating.

... plenty of sleep, little stress

A regular daily timetable is also good for the figure. This does not mean that you must plan your day according to a set pattern, but you should allow your body enough sleep, because that is when the growth hormone can do its fat-reducing work best. And try to reduce stress and switch off occasionally. Continual stress makes you fat, because it stimulates the craving for sweet things.

... regular meals

Never let things get to the stage where a craving makes you stuff yourself with every conceivable unhealthy food. Eat three, or better still five, regular meals a day and don't worry that eating frequently might make you fat, as the opposite is true. If you keep your blood-sugar level stable in this way, you will never run the risk of a sharp rise in insulin level piling the kilos onto your hips.

Start now.

Has all this made you feel hungry now? That's great! The recipes on the following pages, which you can choose from according to your heart's desire and without a guilty conscience, will give you plenty of inspiration for varied and satisfying meals.

Breakfast –
for a great start

Apple muesli

for an early start

Serves 4

4 small apples
3 tbsp lemon juice
120 g jumbo rolled oats
4 tsp honey
1 kg kefir
2 oranges

Preparation time: approx. 5 minutes
Per portion approx.
402 kcal/1690 kJ
14 g P, 7 g F, 74 g CH

1 Wash and core the apples, then grate coarsely without peeling and tip into a small bowl. Mix immediately with the lemon juice.

2 Add the oats and honey and mix with the grated apples. Pour over the kefir.

3 Peel the oranges, cut in slices and arrange on top of the muesli.

Fruit muesli

with pears

1 Toast the sunflower seeds in a dry pan. Wash and dry the pears, trim, peel, core and dice.

2 Divide the cornflakes between 4 bowls, add the pears and drizzle with the honey. Add the milk and serve sprinkled with sunflower seeds.

Serves 4

4 tbsp sunflower seeds
4 pears
12 tbsp cornflakes
4 tbsp honey
600–700 ml milk

Preparation time: approx.
10 minutes
Per portion approx.
260 kcal/1092 kJ
8 g P, 8 g F, 38 g CH

Fruit and muesli trifle
with yoghurt

Serves 4

100 g each of apricot, mango
and peach flesh

40 g dried apple rings

25 g dried cherries

450 ml unsweetened apple
juice

6 cardamoms

6 cloves

1 cinnamon stick

300 g natural yoghurt

100 g sugar-free crunchy
muesli

a little muesli and dried fruit
segments for garnishing

Preparation time: approx.
30 minutes (plus cooking
and cooling time)
Per portion approx.
260 kcal/1092 kJ
7 g P, 2 g F, 48 g CH

1 Put the apricot, mango and peach flesh in a pan with the dried apple rings and cherries. Add the apple juice, mix in the spices and heat. Bring the mixture to the boil and simmer for 15 minutes until the fruits are soft. Leave to cool in the pan.

2 Remove the spices, purée the fruit compote and refrigerate for about 1 hour. Spoon the purée into dessert glasses in layers with the yoghurt and crunchy muesli. Sprinkle with a little muesli, garnish with dried fruit and serve.

Junket with apricot purée

Serves 3–4

2 apples
2 tsp lemon juice
250 g junket
200 g ripe apricots
100 g honey
a few leaves of lemon balm
apple segments

Preparation time: approx.
20 minutes
Per portion approx. 131 kcal/553 kJ
2 g P, 1 g F, 28 g CH

1 Peel the apples, remove the cores and grate. Fold the apples and lemon juice into the junket.

2 For the fruit purée, wash the apricots, cut in half and remove the stones. Mix with the honey and purée. Mix the lemon balm leaves into the fruit purée, reserving a few for decoration.

3 Pour the junket into a bowl and pour the apricot purée over it. Garnish with lemon balm leaves and apple segments.

Porridge
with nuts and maple syrup

Serves 4

625 ml unsweetened apple
  juice
½ tsp ground cinnamon
1 pinch salt
140 g rolled oats
70 g dried cranberries
4 tbsp maple syrup
70 g chopped almonds

Preparation time: approx.
15 minutes (plus cooking time)
Per portion approx.
317 kcal/1327 kJ
6 g P, 9 g F, 47 g CH

1 In a pan bring the apple juice, 125 ml water, cinnamon and salt to the boil. Add the oats, cranberries and maple syrup and mix in. Bring the mixture to the boil and simmer for about 10 minutes, stirring continuously.

2 Fold in the chopped almonds and serve.

Honey quark **with almonds**

Serves 4

400 g low-fat quark
125 ml milk
2 tbsp honey
grated peel of ½ untreated
    lime
2 tbsp ground almonds
1 pinch ground vanilla
3 tbsp cream

Preparation time: approx.
15 minutes
Per portion approx. 156 kcal/655 kJ
15 g P, 5 g F, 10 g CH

1 Mix the low-fat quark with the milk, honey and grated lime peel until creamy.

2 Mix in the ground almonds and ground vanilla. Lastly beat the cream stiff and fold into the quark. Serve immediately.

Strawberry
and cottage cheese breakfast

1 In a pan toast the rolled oats in oil until light brown, stirring continuously. Tip onto a plate and leave to cool.

2 Wash the strawberries, pat dry, trim and cut in four. Mix the cottage cheese with the oats and spoon into 4 individual bowls. Top with the strawberries and serve.

Serves 4

80 g jumbo rolled oats
1 tbsp sunflower oil
400 g strawberries
400 g cottage cheese

Preparation time: approx.
10 minutes (plus toasting time)
Per portion approx. 125 kcal/525 kJ
15 g P, 2 g F, 10 g CH

Chilled buttermilk soup
with peaches

Serves 4

500 ml buttermilk
300 g natural yoghurt
4 tbsp instant oat flakes
4 tbsp honey
250 g raspberries
2 peaches
4 sprigs mint

Preparation time: approx.
10 minutes
Per portion approx.
240 kcal/1004 kJ
9 g P, 4 g F, 37 g CH

1 In a bowl, mix the buttermilk with the yoghurt, oats and honey with a hand blender until smooth. Hull the raspberries, wash and pat dry.

2 Wash and dry the peaches, cut in half, remove the stones and cut the flesh in small cubes.

3 Pour the buttermilk mixture into 4 individual bowls. Top with raspberries and pieces of peach. Wash the mint, shake dry and pick off the leaves. Serve garnished with mint leaves.

ACE juice with almond butter

Serves 4

2 peaches
6 untreated oranges
200 ml unsweetened pear
  juice
2 tbsp organic almond butter

Preparation time: approx.
15 minutes
Per portion approx. 208 kcal/874 kJ
3 g P, 3 g F, 38 g CH

1 Wash the peaches, plunge briefly in boiling water, remove the skins and stones and dice the flesh.

2 Squeeze 5 of the oranges, wash and dry the remaining orange and cut into 4 slices. Purée the peach flesh with the orange juice, pear juice and almond butter. Pour into 4 glasses and garnish each with a slice of orange before serving.

Breakfast shake
with blueberries

1 Pick over the blueberries, remove any remaining stalks, wash and leave to drain in a colander. Then purée the blueberries in a blender together with the kefir.

2 Mix in the wheatgerm and oats and sweeten with a little honey if desired. Pour the shake into 4 glasses and serve immediately, before the oat flakes swell.

Serves 4

400 g blueberries
750 g kefir
4 tbsp wheatgerm
4 tbsp rolled oats
honey as desired

Preparation time: approx.
15 minutes
Per portion approx. 166 kcal/697 kJ
9 g P, 4 g F, 18 g CH

Grapefruit smoothie

Serves 4

100 g strawberries
  (fresh or frozen)
4 pink grapefruit
2 bananas, not fully ripe
300 g natural yoghurt
2 tbsp instant oat flakes
2 tbsp strawberry syrup

Preparation time: approx.
15 minutes
Per portion approx. 179 kcal/748 kJ
7 g P, 1 g F, 33 g CH

1 If using fresh strawberries, wash, pat dry and hull. Peel the grapefruit, making sure you remove all the white pith. Cut the segments out of the dividing membrane, remove the pips and reserve any juice. Squeeze out the membranes, as they usually still contain a little juice.

2 Peel the bananas, cut in pieces and put in a blender with the strawberries, grapefruit segments and grapefruit juice. Add the yoghurt, oats and strawberry syrup, mix thoroughly and serve.

Carrot smoothie

1 Wash and dry the apples and carrots. Cut the apples in four and remove the cores; trim and peel the carrots and cut in pieces. Purée together in a blender.

2 Flavour with maple syrup and lemon juice – freshly squeezed if possible. Add sufficient apple juice to give the smoothie the desired consistency. Add ice cubes if desired and serve immediately.

Serves 4

4 tart apples
4 carrots
2 tsp maple syrup
2 tbsp lemon juice
unsweetened apple juice to
    dilute
ice cubes

Preparation time: approx.
10 minutes
Per portion approx. 149 kcal/624 kJ
1 g P, 0 g F, 36 g CH

Scrambled egg
with salmon strips

Serves 4

8 eggs
2 tbsp soy sauce
cayenne pepper
2 tbsp freshly chopped dill
3 spring onions
200 g smoked salmon
3 tbsp rapeseed oil
coriander leaves for
   garnishing

Preparation time: approx.
15 minutes (plus cooking time)
Per portion approx.
317 kcal/1331 kJ
26 g P, 19 g F, 7 g CH

1 Beat the eggs with the soy sauce, cayenne pepper and freshly chopped dill. Wash, dry and trim the spring onions and cut in rings. Cut the smoked salmon in strips.

2 Heat the oil in a pan and lightly brown the spring onions. Add the beaten eggs and salmon strips and fry gently until the eggs begin to set.

3 Garnish with coriander and serve with fresh wholegrain bread.

Cream cheese spread
with olives

1 Put the cream cheese and yoghurt in a bowl and mix until smooth. Chop the olives, peel the garlic clove and chop finely, and add both to the cheese. Wash the basil, shake dry and chop the leaves. Stir into the cheese mixture and season with pepper.

2 Toast the sesame seeds in a dry pan and grind to a paste in a mortar with a pinch of salt. Mix into the spread. Serve with multigrain baguettes.

Serves 4

125 g low-fat cream cheese
75 g natural yoghurt
80 g stoned black olives
1 garlic clove
1 bunch basil
pepper
1 tsp sesame seeds
sea salt

Preparation time: approx.
15 minutes (plus toasting time)
Per portion approx. 222 kcal/932 kJ
5 g P, 19 g F, 7 g CH

Wholegrain crêpes
with fruit

Serves 4

100 g wholegrain wheat flour
250 ml low-fat milk
3 eggs
3 tbsp honey
1 pinch salt
1 tbsp sunflower oil
3 tbsp butter
1 tbsp sugar
200 g rhubarb
100 g natural yoghurt
whole milk
100 g raspberries

Preparation time: approx.
30 minutes
Per portion approx. 111 kcal/466 kJ
5 g P, 3 g F, 14 g CH

1 Tip the flour into a bowl with the milk, eggs, honey and a pinch of salt and mix to a smooth batter. Then mix in the oil. A little at a time heat 2 tablespoons of butter in a pan and fry 6-8 thin crêpes. Drain on kitchen roll and keep warm.

2 Melt the remaining butter in a pan and caramelise the sugar, stirring continuously. Wash, dry and trim the rhubarb, cut in pieces and add to the pan. Add 100 ml water and stew the rhubarb for 15 minutes until tender. Mix the yoghurt with a few tablespoons of whole milk until nice and runny and pour over the rhubarb.

3 Pick over the raspberries, wash, pat dry, add to the pan and warm gently. Spread the fruit over the crêpes, roll up and serve warm.

Fruit spread

Serves 4

150 g strawberries
150 g raspberries
150 g blossom honey
2 tsp grated rind of
   1 untreated lemon
20 g chopped pistachios

Preparation time: approx.
15 minutes
Per portion approx. 171 kcal/718 kJ
1 g P, 1 g F, 33 g CH

1 Hull and wash the strawberries and raspberries and leave to drain.

2 Purée the berries and honey finely in a
blender.

3 Lastly mix the lemon rind and pistachios into
the fruit purée.

Apricot spread

with lemon balm

1 Wash and dry the apricots, remove the stones and purée. Wash the lemon balm, shake dry and chop.

2 Mix 50 g of the fruit purée with the maple syrup, agar-agar, lemon balm and lemon juice.

3 Bring the remaining apricot purée to the boil and stir in the agar-agar mixture. Boil fiercely for 2 minutes, then pour immediately into screw-top jars that have been rinsed in hot water. Leave the jars of spread to cool.

Makes 3–4 jars

500 g apricots
10 leaves lemon balm
3 tbsp maple syrup
2 tsp agar-agar
juice of ½ lemon

Preparation time: approx.
20 minutes (plus cooking and cooling time)
Per 20 g portion approx.
91 kcal/382 kJ
2 g P, 1 g F, 18 g CH

Snacks for slimming

Raw vegetables with dip

Serves 3–4

2 sticks celery
2 courgettes
1 red pepper
½ cucumber
4 carrots
2 chicory heads

Dip:

80 g single cream
2 tbsp lemon juice
2 tbsp freshly grated
   horseradish
1 tsp honey
sea salt
pepper
2 tbsp freshly chopped mixed
   herbs

Preparation time: approx.
20 minutes
Per portion approx. 172 kcal/722 kJ
5 g P, 8 g F, 16 g CH

1 Trim and wash the vegetables, peel the carrots and cucumber, remove the seeds from the pepper and cut the vegetables in thin sticks. Cut the chicory heads in half, remove the bitter hearts and separate the leaves.

2 For the dip, mix the cream and lemon juice until smooth and then mix in the horse-radish and honey. Season with salt and pepper and sprinkle with herbs.

Raw kohlrabi
with apple

1 Wash the kohlrabi, peel and cut in thin slices. Wash the apples, peel, remove the cores and slice the flesh thinly. Mix the kohlrabi and apples together in a bowl. Squeeze the lemon and mix in the juice.

2 Mix together the quark and orange juice with a little salt, pepper, a pinch of nutmeg and the olive oil, and pour over the kohlrabi and apple. Sprinkle with chive rings and serve.

Serves 4

2 kohlrabi bulbs
3 apples
1 lemon
300 g low-fat quark
juice of ½ orange
sea salt
pepper
nutmeg
2 tbsp olive oil
2 tbsp chive rings for garnishing

Preparation time: approx. 20 minutes
Per portion approx. 154 kcal/647 kJ
12 g P, 3 g F, 17 g CH

Artichoke hearts
in tomato sauce

Serves 4

800 g tomatoes
3 tbsp olive oil
1 garlic clove
4 tbsp tomato paste
sea salt
pepper
16 artichoke hearts
  (from a jar)
1 tbsp freshly chopped chervil

Preparation time: approx.
20 minutes (plus cooking time)
Per portion approx. 84 kcal/353 kJ
3 g P, 4 g F, 7 g CH

1 Wash the tomatoes and cut a cross in the skins. Plunge briefly in boiling water, peel, remove the stalk ends and seeds and dice the flesh.

2 Heat the oil in a pan. Peel the garlic clove, chop finely and brown lightly in the hot oil. Add the diced tomatoes and crush. Stir in the tomato paste and season with a little salt and pepper.

3 Drain the artichoke hearts, add to the tomato sauce, cover and simmer for about 10 minutes. Reduce the sauce until thick and creamy and sprinkle with chervil. Serve with fresh whole-grain rolls.

Roll filled with radishes, avocado and tomato

1 Cut the roll in half. Mix the quark with the tomato purée and spread on both halves of the roll. Slice the avocado and drizzle with lemon juice.

2 Cover the bottom half with slices of cucumber and tomato, then with avocado. Chop the radishes and sprinkle the bottom half of the roll with radishes and parsley. Place the upper half of the roll on top.

For 1 roll

1 wholegrain roll
15 g low-fat quark
1 tbsp tomato purée
¼ avocado
1 tsp lemon juice
3 slices cucumber
2 slices tomato
2 radishes
1 tbsp freshly chopped parsley

Preparation time: approx. 10 minutes
Per portion approx. 685 kcal/2877 kJ
10 g P, 55 g F, 35 g CH

Snacks 65

Cucumber raita

Serves 4

1 cucumber

150 g sour cream 10% fat

250 g natural yoghurt

2 tbsp single cream

½ bunch coriander

½ bunch mint

2 green chillies

1 red chilli

sea salt

pepper

1 tbsp each cumin, mustard, coriander and black cumin seeds

coriander and mint for garnishing

Preparation time: approx.
25 minutes (plus time to draw)
Per portion approx. 108 kcal/539 kJ
4 g P, 9 g F, 6 g CH

1 Wash, dry and trim the cucumber, and dice the flesh.

2 Mix together the sour cream, yoghurt and single cream and add to the cucumber. Wash and dry the herbs, chop the leaves finely and add to the cucumber mixture. Wash the chillies, cut in half lengthways, remove the seeds, cut in strips and add to the mixture. Season to taste with salt and pepper and leave to draw in the refrigerator for approx. 20 minutes.

3 Toast the remaining spices in a dry pan until the seeds begin to split and release their aroma. Tip the seeds over the cucumber raita and serve garnished with coriander and mint leaves.

Green spelt rissoles
with leeks

1 Bring the ground green spelt to the boil in hot vegetable stock, remove from the heat and leave to swell for 10 minutes.

2 Peel and chop the onion and garlic clove. Wash and trim the leek and cut in thin rings. Heat 1 tablespoon of rapeseed oil and lightly brown the onion, garlic clove and leek, stirring continuously.

3 Mix the vegetables with the green spelt, eggs, curry powder, salt and pepper and work into a smooth dough. Form the dough into 8 rissoles and fry on both sides in the remaining hot rapeseed oil until crisp.

Serves 4

200 g ground green spelt
400 ml vegetable stock
1 onion
1 garlic clove
1 leek
2 tbsp rapeseed oil
2 eggs
½ tsp curry powder
sea salt
pepper

Preparation time: approx. 20 minutes (plus time to swell and cooking time)
Per portion approx. 127 kcal/533 kJ
5 g P, 3 g F, 17 g CH

Garlic prawns
with chilli

Serves 4

5 garlic cloves
½ bunch parsley
24 large, peeled prawns
3 tbsp olive oil
1 dried red chilli
100 ml vegetable stock
24 wooden toothpicks

Preparation time: approx.
10 minutes (plus cooking time)
Per portion approx.
695 kcal/2919 kJ
122 g P, 20 g F, 6 g CH

1 Pre-heat the oven to 200 °C (Gas Mark 6). Peel the garlic and chop finely. Wash the parsley, shake dry and chop finely. Wash the prawns and leave to drain, if necessary devein beforehand.

2 Heat the oil and fry the garlic. Crumble the chilli and add to the pan. Add the parsley and fry for 2 minutes, stirring continuously.

3 Add the prawns and the vegetable stock. Cook in the oven at 200 °C (Gas Mark 6) for about 15 minutes. Spear each prawn with a toothpick and serve in the stock.

Wholegrain muffins
with tuna and courgettes

1 Trim the spring onions and cut in rings. Drain the tuna and shred in small pieces. Trim the courgette and grate finely.

2 Mix together the flour, baking powder, spices and onions. Mix the other ingredients together and fold into the flour.

3 Pre-heat the oven to 180 °C (Gas Mark 4, fan 160 °C). Spoon the mixture into 8 muffin tins and bake for about 20 minutes.

Serves 4

4 spring onions
100 g tuna (tinned)
½ courgette
100 g wholegrain flour
2 tsp baking powder
sea salt
pepper
2 eggs
30 g butter
40 g single cream
vegetable oil for greasing
   the muffin tin

Preparation time approx.
20 minutes (plus baking time)
Per portion approx.
335 kcal/1407 kJ
12 g P, 21 g F, 23 g CH

Beef carpaccio

Serves 4

300 g fillet of beef without fat
and sinews

1 stick celery

2 tbsp lemon juice

6 tbsp olive oil

crystal salt

pepper

40 g Parmesan or Grana
Padano

Preparation time: approx.
20 minutes (plus freezing and
marinating time)

Per portion approx.
260 kcal/1092 kJ
19 g P, 19 g F, 2 g CH

1 Place the beef in the freezer for about 1 hour until lightly frozen. Then cut in wafer-thin slices.

2 Trim and wash the celery and dice the upper part finely. Mix the lemon juice with oil and salt to give a creamy sauce.

3 Arrange the slices of beef on a plate and sprinkle with freshly ground pepper, then drizzle with the sauce.

4 Cover with foil and leave to draw for about 30 minutes. Top with cheese shavings and diced celery.

Tuna carpaccio
with capers

1 Wash and dry the tuna, wrap in foil and place in the freezer for about 2 hours to make it easier to cut.

2 Peel the shallot and chop finely. Mix the olive oil thoroughly with the sherry vinegar, salt and pepper. Then mix in the shallot and the drained capers.

3 Cut the frozen tuna in wafer-thin slices. Arrange these on 4 plates and drizzle with the sauce. Serve with toasted wholegrain baguette.

Serves 4

350 g fresh tuna
1 shallot
2 tbsp olive oil
1 tsp sherry vinegar
sea salt
black pepper
3 tsp small capers

Preparation time: approx.
10 minutes (plus freezing time)
Per portion approx.
280 kcal/1176 kJ
20 g P, 20 g F, 3 g CH

Smoked salmon rolls
on carrot spirals

Serves 4

8 slices smoked salmon
(each 30 g)

1 tbsp mustard

1 tbsp honey

freshly ground pepper

1 bunch dill

4 leaves iceberg lettuce

1 carrot

1 tbsp lemon juice

1 piece fresh horseradish
(approx. 1 cm)

cress and lemon slices for
garnishing

Preparation time: approx.
15 minutes
Per portion approx. 131 kcal/551 kJ
13 g P, 4 g F, 10 g CH

1 Arrange the salmon slices side by side on a work surface. In a bowl, mix together the mustard, honey and a little pepper.

2 Wash the dill, shake dry and chop finely. Mix the dill into the mustard and honey mixture and spread over the salmon slices.

3 Wash and dry the lettuce leaves, remove the thick ends of the stems and cut the leaves in half lengthways. Place the lettuce strips on the salmon slices and roll up.

4 Trim and wash the carrot and peel off spirals with a vegetable peeler or use a spiralizer. Arrange the carrot spirals on a plate with the salmon rolls on top.

5 Top with freshly grated horseradish and drizzle with the lemon juice. Garnish with cress and slices of lemon, and serve.

Tomatoes
with buffalo mozzarella

Serves 4

4 large tomatoes
300 g buffalo mozzarella
1 bunch basil
crystal salt
pepper
4 tbsp olive oil

Preparation time: approx.
20 minutes
Per portion approx.
305 kcal/1282 kJ
15 g P, 26 g F, 3 g CH

1 Wash the tomatoes, remove the stalk ends and cut in slices.

2 Drain the mozzarella and cut in slices. Wash the basil, shake dry and pick off the leaves. Arrange the tomatoes and mozzarella alternately on a large serving dish and top each slice of mozzarella with a basil leaf.

3 Season with salt and freshly ground black pepper and drizzle with the olive oil.

Ham and asparagus rolls

1 Wash the asparagus, peel, cut off the woody ends and cook the stems in boiling salted water for about 20 minutes. Drain and leave to drip.

2 Wrap 2 asparagus stems in each slice of ham to make 8 ham rolls. Tie up with chive stems. Serve with home-made herb quark.

Serves 4

1 kg white asparagus
salt
8 slices cooked ham
chives for garnishing

Preparation time: approx.
15 minutes (plus cooking time)
Per portion approx. 91 kcal/382 kJ
17 g P, 3 g F, 6 g CH

Energy drink

with vegetables

Serves 4

1 bunch dill
1 cucumber
400 ml tomato juice
200 ml carrot juice
1 tbsp olive oil
Tabasco for flavouring

Preparation time: approx.
10 minutes
Per portion approx. 61 kcal/256 kJ
2 g P, 3 g F, 6 g CH

1 Wash the dill, shake dry, set a few sprigs aside, pick the fronds off the remainder and chop finely. Wash, peel and trim the cucumber and cut in chunks, reserving a few fairly thick slices for decoration.

2 Purée the cucumber with the dill, tomato juice, carrot juice and olive oil. Flavour the drink with Tabasco and pour into 4 glasses. Decorate with dill and cucumber slices.

Refreshing
cucumber smoothie

1 Wash and peel the cucumber, cut in half lengthways and scoop out the seeds with a teaspoon. Wash, trim and dry the pepper. Wash and trim the spring onion. Cut all of these in pieces.

2 Put all the ingredients except for the crushed ice in a blender and purée until you have the desired consistency. Then freeze for at least 30 minutes.

3 Transfer the smoothie to 4 glasses, top up with crushed ice and stir once. Serve immediately.

Serves 4

1 cucumber
1 red pepper
1 spring onion
2 glasses tomato juice
6 tsp lemon juice
½ tsp sea salt
½ tsp freshly ground pepper
½ tsp Tabasco
a little crushed Ice

Preparation time: approx. 15 minutes (plus freezing time)
Per portion approx. 41 kcal/168 kJ
2 g P, 0 g F, 8 g CH

Tomato kefir
with chives

Serves 4

600 ml kefir
400 g puréed tomatoes
4 tsp lemon juice
4 tbsp chives, in rings
a little garlic powder
pepper
sea salt
cherry tomatoes and basil for
  decoration

Preparation time: approx.
10 minutes
Per portion approx. 127 kcal/531 kJ
7 g P, 5 g F, 12 g CH

1 Purée the kefir, puréed tomatoes, lemon juice and chives thoroughly in a blender. Season with garlic powder, pepper and salt.

2 Pour into decorative glasses and serve decorated with cherry tomatoes and basil.

Avocado smoothie

1 Peel the avocados, cut open, remove the stones, cut the flesh in pieces and drizzle with the lemon juice.

2 Wash, dry and trim the pepper and cut in pieces. Put the avocado, pepper, sweetcorn, quark, sunflower seeds and ice in a blender.

3 Mix thoroughly and season with a little salt. Serve immediately.

Serves 4

2 ripe avocados
2 tbsp lemon juice
2 small yellow pepper
100 g cooked sweetcorn
200 g low-fat quark
4 tsp sunflower seeds
120 g crushed ice
a little sea salt

Preparation time: approx. 10 minutes
Per portion approx. 313 kcal/1309 kJ
14 g P, 17 g F, 24 g CH

Soups and salads
for fitness

Minestrone with pesto

Serves 4

1.5 litres vegetable stock
3 aubergines
100 g courgettes
1 savoy cabbage
50 g pumpkin
4 tomatoes
100 g green beans
3 potatoes
150 g white beans
30 g dried porcini mushrooms
2 tbsp olive oil
100 g natural rice
100 g pesto
sea salt
pepper

Preparation time: approx.
35 minutes
Per portion approx.
343 kcal/1436 kJ
16 g P, 7 g F, 58 g CH

1 Bring the vegetable stock to the boil in a pan. Dice the aubergines and courgettes, cut the cabbage in small strips, peel and dice the pumpkin and cut the tomatoes in small pieces. Trim the green beans and cut in small pieces. Peel and dice the potatoes. Soak the dried mushrooms and chop small.

2 Add the white beans and vegetables to the boiling water. Then add the mushrooms and oil. Simmer the soup for about 20 minutes, then add the rice and simmer for a further 20 minutes. Before serving, stir the pesto into the soup and season to taste with salt and pepper.

French
herb soup

Serves 4

1 shallot
150 g sorrel
100 g leaf spinach
1 bunch celery leaves
1 bunch watercress
1 bunch chervil
1 bunch flat-leaf parsley
1 kg floury potatoes
1½ cucumbers
3 tbsp olive oil
sea salt
3 tbsp single cream
freshly ground pepper

Preparation time: approx. 30 minutes
(plus cooking time)
Per portion approx. 124 kcal/552 kJ
9 g P, 13 g F, 40 g CH

1 Peel the shallot and chop finely. Trim and wash the leafy vegetables and herbs and shake dry. Set aside a few herb leaves for garnishing. Peel, wash and dice the potatoes.

2 Trim and wash the cucumber, cut in half, scoop out the seeds with a teaspoon and dice the cucumber finely. Heat the olive oil in a pan and add the leafy vegetables, herbs and cucumber. Cover and fry gently for 2 minutes, without letting the vegetables and herbs brown.

3 Add 1.5 litres of water to the pan, salt, add the potatoes and boil for 25 minutes.

4 At the end of the cooking time sieve the soup. Mix in the single cream with a hand-held mixer. Season to taste with salt and pepper. Serve the soup garnished with herb leaves.

Sauerkraut soup
with paprika

Serves 4

1 onion

1 tbsp sunflower oil

500 g sauerkraut (from a jar)

1 red pepper, de-seeded and
diced

2 potatoes, peeled and diced

1 tsp each of sweet and hot
paprika powder

1.25 litres vegetable stock

1 bay leaf

2 cloves

1 pinch ground cumin

sea salt

pepper

2 tbsp chopped parsley

Preparation time: approx.
15 minutes
Per portion approx. 154 kcal/645 kJ
5 g P, 4 g F, 20 g CH

1 Peel and chop the onion. Heat 1 tablespoon of oil in a pan and lightly brown the onion.

2 Drain the sauerkraut, add the diced red pepper and potatoes and fry briefly with the onion.

3 Stir the sweet and hot paprika powder into the vegetables, then add the vegetable stock. Add the bay leaf, cloves and a pinch of ground cumin, cover and simmer for about 20 minutes.

4 Season the soup to taste with salt and pepper and serve sprinkled with chopped parsley.

Potato and rocket soup

Serves 3–4

800 g potatoes
2 garlic cloves
150 g rocket
1.4 litres vegetable stock
2 tbsp olive oil
sea salt
pepper

Preparation time: approx.
30 minutes (plus cooking time)
Per portion approx.
270 kcal/1134 kJ
12 g P, 10 g F, 30 g CH

1 Peel and dice the potatoes. Peel and chop the garlic. Wash the rocket, shake dry and cut in strips.

2 Heat the stock and cook the potatoes and garlic in it for about 15 minutes. Add the rocket and simmer for 2 minutes. Purée the soup with the oil. Season to taste with salt and pepper.

3 Pour the soup into heatproof glasses or soup bowls.

Vegetable soup
with courgettes

1 Peel the onion and carrots and cut in rings or slices. Trim, wash and dice the celery. Trim the courgettes and cut in slices. Peel and dice the potatoes.

2 Heat the oil in a large pan and add the vegetables. Brown lightly for about 5 minutes, then add the vegetable stock. Simmer for about 30 minutes, until the vegetables are *al dente*.

3 Season the soup with salt and pepper and serve sprinkled with parsley.

Serves 4

1 onion
3 carrots
1 stick celery
2 courgettes
2 potatoes
3 tbsp rapeseed oil
1.5 litres vegetable stock
sea salt
pepper
2 tbsp freshly chopped parsley

Preparation time: approx.
20 minutes (plus cooking time)
Per portion approx.
305 kcal/1281 kJ
5 g P, 22 g F, 22 g CH

French fish soup

Serves 4

1 kg mixed ready-to-cook fish
1 onion
4 potatoes
4 tomatoes
½ fennel bulb
4 tbsp olive oil
4 bay leaves
herbes de Provence
sea salt
pepper
1 packet saffron
4 garlic cloves
500 ml vegetable stock
500 ml fish stock

Preparation time: approx.
25 minutes (plus cooking and
drawing time)
Per portion approx.
483 kcal/2029 kJ
42 g P, 19 g F, 23 g CH

1 Cut the fish in pieces. Peel and chop the onion. Wash, peel and grate the potatoes. Wash the tomatoes, remove the stalk ends and dice. Trim the fennel and cut in strips.

2 Heat the olive oil in a pan and lightly brown the onion. Add the potatoes, tomatoes and fennel and cook with the onion. Add the bay leaves, herbes de Provence and spices. Peel the garlic and crush into the pan. Simmer for 10 minutes, then add the fish and cook for 3 minutes.

3 Heat both kinds of stock, mix with the fish and vegetables, remove from the heat and leave the soup to draw for 10 minutes.

Cabbage
soup with bamboo shoots

1 Soak the jelly ear fungi overnight. The next day drain and cut in thin strips. Tip the bamboo shoots into a sieve and leave to drain.

2 Trim the cabbage and leek, wash thoroughly and cut these and the bamboo shoots in thin strips.

3 Cook the rice noodles following the instructions on the packet and drain. Bring the vegetable stock to the boil with the leek, bamboo shoots and mushrooms and simmer for 20 minutes. Then add the cabbage and cook for a further 5 minutes. Flavour to taste with soy sauce.

4 Put the noodles in soup bowls, pour over the hot soup and serve immediately.

Serves 4

5 dried jelly ear fungi
1 small jar bamboo shoots (230 g drained weight)
250 g Chinese cabbage
1 leek
100 g thin rice noodles
1¼ litres vegetable stock
1 tbsp soy sauce

Preparation time: approx.
20 minutes (plus soaking and cooking time)
Per portion approx.
305 kcal/1281 kJ
41 g P, 6 g F, 40 g CH

Pepper salad with coriander

Serves 4

2 green peppers
1 yellow pepper
3 large tomatoes
1 garlic clove
1 tbsp sherry vinegar
5 tbsp olive oil
sea salt
pepper
½ bunch coriander

Preparation time: approx.
45 minutes (plus cooking time and
time to draw)
Per portion approx. 103 kcal/433 kJ
2 g P, 7 g F, 7 g CH

1 Pre-heat the oven to 200 °C (fan 180 °C, Gas Mark 6). Wash and trim the peppers, cut in half and remove the seeds. Arrange with the cut edges down on a baking sheet and roast in the oven until the skins go black. Remove the peppers from the oven, leave to cool, remove the skins and cut in pieces.

2 Cut a cross in the tomatoes at the stalk end, blanch briefly in boiling water and rinse in cold water. Peel, remove the seeds and stalk ends and cut the flesh in 2 cm pieces. Peel and crush the garlic clove.

3 Put the tomatoes and peppers in a bowl. Make a dressing with the garlic, vinegar, oil, salt and pepper and pour over the salad. Leave to draw for 10 minutes. Decorate with coriander leaves and serve.

Soya bean sprout
salad **with spring onions**

1 Wash the bean sprouts thoroughly and leave to drain. Blanch for 1 minute in 1 litre boiling salted water, drain, rinse in cold water and leave to drain.

2 Make a dressing with the soy sauce, rice-wine vinegar, sesame oil and a little salt, and mix in a bowl with the bean sprouts. Trim, wash and dry the spring onions and cut in rings. Fold into the salad, and serve.

Serves 4

500 g soya bean sprouts
sea salt
2 tbsp light soy sauce
1 tbsp rice-wine vinegar
2 tbsp sesame oil
2 spring onions

Preparation time: approx.
15 minutes
Per portion approx. 101 kcal/424 kJ
8 g P, 5 g F, 7 g CH

Portuguese salad

Serves 4

2 large firm tomatoes
2 green pepper
3 carrots
1 onion
1 egg
1 bunch parsley
5 radishes
1 lettuce
1 tbsp freshly chopped dill
4 tbsp olive oil
4 tbsp vinegar
sea salt
pepper

Preparation time: approx.
20 minutes
Per portion approx. 113 kcal/474 kJ
4 g P, 7 g F, 6 g CH

1 Wash the tomatoes, remove the stalk ends and cut in slices. Trim and wash the peppers, remove the seeds and cut in strips. Wash, peel and grate the carrots.

2 Peel the onion and cut in thin rings. Hard-boil the egg, peel and cut in slices. Wash and dry the parsley, pick off the leaves and chop. Slice the radishes. Wash the lettuce, spin dry and pick off the leaves.

3 Tip the vegetables into a salad bowl. Make a dressing with the dill, olive oil, vinegar, salt and pepper. Add to the salad and mix well. Top with slices of egg and sprinkle with parsley.

Chicory salad
with mandarin and honey dressing

1 Trim and wash the chicory, cut out the bitter stalks in a cone shape and cut the leaves in strips approx. 2 cm wide. Peel the grapefruit, making sure you remove the white pith. Carefully separate the segments from the dividing membranes and mix in a bowl with the chicory. Drain the mandarins thoroughly in a sieve and reserve the juice. Mix the mandarins gently into the salad.

2 Mix together the honey, mustard, paprika paste and mandarin juice. Flavour with salt, Tabasco and Worcestershire sauce. Pour over the salad and mix in thoroughly.

Serves 4

4 chicory heads (approx. 500 g)
2 pink grapefruit
175 g tinned mandarin segments
2 tbsp honey
1 tsp mustard
2 tbsp paprika paste
70 ml NFC mandarin juice, unsweetened
sea salt
Tabasco
Worcestershire sauce

Preparation time: approx. 30 minutes
Per portion approx. 125 kcal/556 kJ
3 g P, 1 g F, 24 g CH

Lombardy mushroom salad

Serves 4

400 g porcini mushrooms
200 g chanterelles
200 g oyster mushrooms
1 red chilli
1 garlic clove
1 bunch parsley
8 tbsp olive oil
sea salt
pepper
2 tbsp lemon juice
250 g rocket
2 tbsp balsamic vinegar

Preparation time: approx.
40 minutes
Per portion approx. 392 kcal/1383 kJ
6 g P, 26 g F, 13 g CH

1 Clean the mushrooms with a soft brush. Cut the porcini mushrooms in four and then in smaller pieces. Cut any large chanterelles in half. Cut the oyster mushrooms in pieces. Trim and wash the chilli and chop finely. Peel the garlic clove and chop finely. Wash the parsley, shake dry and chop.

2 Heat 6 tablespoons of oil in a pan and lightly brown the mushrooms. Add the chilli, garlic and parsley. Flavour to taste with salt, pepper and lemon juice. Leave to draw for approx. 4 minutes.

3 Trim and wash the rocket, spin dry and cut off the stems. In a bowl, mix together the balsamic vinegar and the remaining olive oil. Season well with salt and pepper.

4 Mix together the rocket and salad dressing. Remove the mushrooms from the pan and drain a little.

5 Arrange the rocket on plates, top with the mushrooms and serve.

Asparagus salad
with strawberries

Serves 4

600 g white asparagus
sea salt
250 g strawberries
3 tbsp freshly squeezed
  orange juice
80 g single cream
2 tbsp tarragon vinegar
2 tbsp sunflower oil
pepper
1 tsp green peppercorns

Preparation time: approx. 30
minutes (plus cooking time)
Per portion approx. 79 kcal/332 kJ
4 g P, 3 g F, 5 g CH

1 Wash and peel the asparagus, cut off the ends and cut the sticks in pieces about 3 cm long. Cook *al dente* in boiling salted water. Drain and leave to cool.

2 Trim and wash the strawberries and cut in four. Mix together the orange juice, single cream, vinegar and oil and season to taste with salt and pepper.

3 Mix the asparagus and strawberries together in a bowl and pour over the dressing. Garnish with green peppercorns and serve.

Cauliflower and broccoli salad

1 Wash the broccoli and cauliflower florets. Bring the vegetable stock to the boil, add the broccoli and cauliflower, cover and cook *al dente* for about 7 minutes. Drain and leave to cool.

2 Wash, dry and trim the spring onions and cut in thin rings. Peel the hard-boiled egg and chop finely.

3 Mix together the yoghurt, single cream, fruit vinegar, lemon juice and curry powder, and season with salt and pepper to taste.

4 Mix the cauliflower and broccoli with the dressing and the onion rings. Wash and dry the chives and cut in rings. Garnish the salad with egg and chives.

Serves 4

400 g each of broccoli and
 cauliflower florets
300 ml vegetable stock
½ bunch spring onions
1 hard-boiled egg
150 g natural yoghurt
50 g single cream
2 tbsp fruit vinegar
juice of ½ lemon
1 tsp curry powder
sea salt
pepper
½ bunch chives

Preparation time: approx. 25 minutes
(plus cooking and cooling time)
Per portion approx. 149 kcal/628 kJ
10 g P, 7 g F, 10 g CH

Brussels sprout salad
with celeriac

Serves 4

500 g Brussels sprouts
500 ml vegetable stock
2 carrots
200 g celeriac
2 spring onions
150 g light cream with herbs
sea salt
pepper
2 tbsp lemon juice
nutmeg

Preparation time: approx. 25 minutes
Per portion approx. 191 kcal/783 kJ
9 g P, 13 g F, 9 g CH

1 Trim the Brussels sprouts and cook *al dente* in the vegetable stock for about 10 minutes. Drain, reserving the stock, leave to drip, and transfer to a bowl.

2 Peel the carrots and celeriac and cut both in thin sticks, blanch in the vegetable stock and add to the bowl with the Brussels sprouts. Trim the spring onions, cut in rings and add to the bowl.

3 Flavour the herb single cream with salt, pepper, lemon juice and nutmeg, and pour over the vegetables.

Oak-leaf lettuce

and avocado salad

1 Peel and fillet the grapefruit. Peel the avocados, cut in half, remove the stones and dice the flesh. Wash and trim the oak-leaf salad, spin dry and cut in small pieces.

2 Cut a cross in the stalk ends of the tomatoes, plunge in boiling water, rinse in cold water and remove the skins. Then remove the seeds and dice the flesh. Mix with the grapefruit segments, diced avocado and oak-leaf lettuce.

3 Make a dressing with the lemon juice, honey, olive oil, salt and pepper, and drizzle over the salad. Wash the parsley, shake dry, chop and sprinkle over the salad before serving.

Serves 4

4 pink grapefruit
2 avocados
1 oak-leaf lettuce
4 tomatoes
juice of 3 lemons
3 tbsp honey
6 tbsp olive oil
sea salt
pepper
½ bunch parsley

Preparation time: approx.
20 minutes
Per portion approx.
483 kcal/2029 kJ
5 g P, 35 g F, 32 g CH

Vegetarian
main dishes

Colourful vegetable stir-fry

Serves 4

3 red onions

2 garlic cloves

2 small aubergines

2 small courgettes

4 beef tomatoes

2 peppers

4 tbsp sesame oil

sea salt

freshly ground pepper

mustard seeds

ground cumin

1–2 stems Thai basil

1–2 stems lemon grass or
  1 tbsp dried lemon grass

500 ml vegetable stock

2–3 tbsp peeled sesame
  seeds

Preparation time: approx.
25 minutes (plus cooking time)
Per portion approx. 192 kcal/809 kJ
5 g P, 13 g F, 15 g CH

1 Peel the onions and garlic cloves and dice finely. Trim and wash the aubergines and courgettes, cut in half lengthways and in triangular pieces the thickness of a finger. Peel the tomatoes, cut in half, remove the seeds and cut in small pieces. Cut the peppers in half, remove the seeds, wash and cut in chunks.

2 Heat the oil in a wok and stir-fry each vegetable separately for approx. 2–3 minutes. Then put all the vegetables together in the wok and season with salt, pepper, mustard seed and cumin.

3 Trim and wash the herbs and chop finely. Add to the vegetables and add the vegetable stock. Boil for approx. 3 minutes. Toast the sesame seeds in a dry pan and sprinkle over the vegetables.

Steamed savoy cabbage parcels

Serves 4

200 g natural rice
sea salt
12 savoy cabbage leaves
200 g button mushrooms
1 bunch spring onions
5 tomatoes
200 g bean sprouts
4–6 tbsp soy sauce
pepper
300 ml vegetable stock

Preparation time: approx. 25 minutes
(plus cooking time)
Per portion approx. 240 kcal/1007 kJ
9 g P, 2 g F, 46 g CH

1 Cook the rice in salted water following the instructions on the packet and drain thoroughly. Set aside and keep warm. Trim and wash the cabbage leaves. Blanch in salted water for about 1 minute, rinse in cold water and leave to drain. When cooled, cut the central ribs of the leaves flat.

2 Trim the mushrooms, brush clean, wash and dry if necessary, then cut in small cubes. Trim and wash the spring onions and cut in thin rings. Wash the tomatoes, cut a cross in the skins, plunge in boiling water, remove the stalk ends, skins and seeds and dice finely. Wash the bean sprouts under cold running water and leave to drain.

3 Mix the vegetables with the bean sprouts and the boiled rice. Season well with the soy sauce and a little freshly ground pepper. Spread out the cabbage leaves. Spoon the rice mixture onto them, smooth over a little and roll up into small parcels, turning the sides in slightly. Tie in place with kitchen string.

4 In a wok, bring the vegetable stock to the boil. Cover and steam the parcels over low heat for about 35 minutes until tender. Then remove from the wok and carefully remove the string.

Boiled artichokes

Serves 4

4 artichokes
5 tbsp lemon juice
6 tbsp wine vinegar
sea salt
pepper
1 hard-boiled egg
2 shallots
1 bunch parsley
1 tbsp capers
4 tbsp olive oil
sugar

Preparation time: approx.
30 minutes (plus cooking time)
Per portion approx.
272 kcal/1144 kJ
8 g P, 12 g F, 12 g CH

1 Wash the artichokes, leave to drain, then cut off the leaf tips with kitchen scissors. Cut off the stalks close to the bases and rub the artichokes with lemon juice. Bring a pan of salted water to the boil and add a few drops of lemon juice. Simmer the artichokes over low heat for approx. 40 minutes, without boiling.

2 Mix the vinegar with salt and pepper. Peel the egg and chop finely. Peel the shallots and cut in small cubes.

3 Wash and dry the parsley and chop the leaves finely. Drain the capers. Mix the parsley and capers with the vinegar and beat in the oil. Flavour to taste with salt, pepper and sugar. Serve the artichokes with the vinaigrette.

Green lentils and vegetables **with yoghurt**

Serves 4

6 tbsp sunflower oil

8 cloves

8 green cardamoms

2 cinnamon sticks
  (approx. 2 cm)

3 red onions

3 garlic cloves

2 red chillies

1 green chilli

2 tbsp freshly grated ginger

1 tsp cumin

350 g Puy lentils

600 ml vegetable stock

5 tbsp lemon juice

5 tbsp natural yoghurt

1 tbsp single cream

½ bunch coriander

black pepper

Preparation time: approx.
30 minutes (plus cooking time)
Per portion: approx.
375 kcal/1575 kJ
21 g P, 8 g F, 49 g CH

1 Heat the oil and toast the cloves, cardamoms and cinnamon. Peel and dice the onions. Peel and crush the garlic cloves. Wash the chillies, cut in half lengthways, remove the seeds and cut in strips. Mix all these together and mix in the ginger and cumin.

2 Wash the lentils and add to the pan, along with the stock. Simmer over low heat for approx. 18 minutes.

3 Mix together the lemon juice, yoghurt and single cream. Wash and dry the coriander, reserve a few leaves for garnishing, chop the remainder finely and stir into the yoghurt mixture. Season with black pepper and serve garnished with coriander leaves.

Steamed tomatoes
with ginger cabbage

Serves 4

---

12 medium tomatoes
½ small white cabbage
100 g ginger root
1 tbsp groundnut oil
2 tbsp powdered ginger
2 tbsp hoisin sauce
a little coriander oil
½ bunch coriander

Preparation time: approx.
40 minutes
Per portion approx. 118 kcal/497 kJ
4 g P, 6 g F, 13 g CH

1 Wash and dry the tomatoes, cut off lids and carefully scrape out the seeds and the hard centres with a small spoon. Remove the outer leaves of the cabbage, cut the cabbage in half, cut out the stem and pull off the leaves. Wash and dry the leaves and cut in fine strips. Peel the ginger and cut in thin slices.

2 Heat the oil in a wok and gently fry the cabbage strips with the powdered ginger and hoisin sauce until tender. Then stuff the tomatoes with the cabbage strips. Put sets of three tomatoes in bamboo baskets and top with slices of ginger.

3 Heat a little water in the wok and pile the baskets on top of one another in the wok. The water should not come in contact with the food being cooked. Close the wok. After 10 minutes swop the upper baskets with the lower ones and steam for a further 10 minutes.

4 Lastly, drizzle the tomatoes with a little coriander oil and, if desired, sprinkle with finely chopped coriander leaves.

Tofu goujons
with oyster mushrooms

Serves 4

200 g tofu
sea salt
pepper
2 tbsp lime juice
½ tsp curry powder
2 tbsp soy sauce
1 onion
4 tbsp olive oil
40 g oyster mushrooms
1 tsp flour
100 g single cream
nutmeg
cayenne pepper
1 spring onion

Preparation time: approx.
15 minutes (plus marinating and
cooking time)
Per portion approx. 152 kcal/640 kJ
9 g P, 8 g F, 2 g CH

1 Cut the tofu in strips and season with salt and pepper. Mix the lime juice with the curry powder and soy sauce and marinate the tofu strips in the mixture for about 15 minutes.

2 Peel and chop the onion and fry gently in 2 tablespoons of hot oil until transparent. Trim the oyster mushrooms, wipe with a damp cloth, cut in small pieces and fry with the onion.

3 Dust the mushrooms and onion with flour and brown. Stir in the single cream. Season with nutmeg and cayenne pepper and simmer for 8 minutes.

4 Drain the tofu strips and fry in a second pan with the remaining oil until crisp. Fold into the mushroom mixture. Trim, wash and dry the spring onion and cut in rings.

5 Serve on individual plates and garnish with the spring onion rings. Serve with rice cooked according to the instructions on the packet.

Spaghetti

with watercress pesto

Serves 4

1 bunch watercress
30 g pine nuts
40 g Parmesan
pepper
6 tbsp olive oil
400 g spaghetti
sea salt

Preparation time: approx.
35 minutes
Per portion approx. 552 kcal/2305 kJ
19 g P, 20 g F, 68 g CH

1 Wash and dry the watercress. Pick off the leaves and chop very finely, together with the pine nuts. Grate the Parmesan finely. Mix together the chopped cress and pine nuts, pepper and 30 g grated Parmesan. Gradually mix in the oil until the mixture is viscous.

2 Cook the spaghetti following the instructions on the packet, drain and leave to drip. Transfer in portions to deep dishes and add a generous tablespoon of the watercress pesto to each portion. If desired, sprinkle with the remaining grated Parmesan and serve.

Potatoes
with herb quark

1 Mix the quark and milk together until nice and creamy. Season with salt and pepper.

2 Wash the herbs, shake dry and chop finely. Mix the herbs into the quark. Leave the quark to draw for 20 minutes, then season again to taste with salt and pepper.

3 Wash the potatoes and boil skin-on in salted water for about 20 minutes. Drain and serve with the herb quark.

Serves 4

500 g low-fat quark
125 ml whole milk
sea salt
pepper
½ bunch parsley
½ bunch chives
¼ bunch lovage
¼ bunch chervil
500 g potatoes

Preparation time: approx.
15 minutes (plus approx.
20 minutes cooking time and
approx. 20 minutes to draw)
Per portion approx.
368 kcal/1543 kJ
38 g P, 2 g F, 48 g CH

Fancy
winter vegetables

Serves 4

2 shallots
250 g carrots
1 leek
200 g celery
100 g white cabbage
1 tbsp rapeseed oil
200 ml vegetable stock
1 tsp arrowroot
80 g single cream
1 tbsp capers
1 pinch paprika powder
sea salt
pepper
nutmeg
2 tbsp freshly chopped
    coriander

Preparation time: approx.
20 minutes (plus cooking time)
Per portion approx. 101 kcal/426 kJ
3 g P, 6 g F, 7 g CH

1 Peel and chop the shallots. Trim, peel and dice the carrots. Wash, dry and trim the leek, and cut in rings.

2 Wash, dry and trim the celery and cut in thin slices. Wash the cabbage and cut in strips.

3 Heat the oil in a pan and fry the shallots until transparent. Then add the other vegetables and fry with the onion.

4 Add 5 tablespoons of vegetable stock and cook for a further 10 minutes. Stir the arrow-root into the remaining vegetable stock until smooth and add to the vegetables.

5 Drain the capers. Mix together the single cream, capers, a pinch of paprika powder, salt, pepper and nutmeg, and stir into the vege-tables. Serve garnished with the chopped cori-ander. Fresh wholegrain bread goes well with this.

Fried fennel

Serves 4

2 fennel bulbs
4 tbsp olive oil
4 tbsp lime juice
2 tsp honey
sea salt
pepper
1 pinch cumin
400 g carrots
1 pomegranate

Preparation time: approx.
25 minutes (plus cooking time)
Per portion approx.
112 kcal/470 kcal
3 g P, 5 g F, 11 g CH

1 Wash and trim the fennel bulbs, cut in half, remove the hard centre and cut the bulbs lengthways in thin slices. Mix 2 tablespoons of oil with the lime juice, honey and spices.

2 Heat the remaining olive oil and fry the fennel slices until they begin to brown. Arrange on a warmed plate and drizzle with a little of the lime marinade.

3 Trim, wash and grate the carrots and mix with remaining marinade. Spread over the fennel. Cut open the pomegranate, remove the seeds and spread them over the fennel and carrots.

Wholegrain spaghetti
with broccoli

1 Trim and wash the broccoli and cut in small pieces. Cook the spaghetti in boiling salted water following the instructions on the packet. 5 minutes before the end of the cooking time, add the broccoli and cook for a further 5 minutes. Peel and chop the garlic.

2 Heat the oil in a wok. Lightly fry the garlic. Drain the spaghetti and broccoli, leave to drip and add to the wok. Add all the other ingredients apart from the sesame oil and coriander and season to taste. Sprinkle with coriander and drizzle with sesame oil.

Serves 3–4

750 g broccoli
400 g wholegrain spaghetti
sea salt
1 garlic clove
3 tbsp olive oil
1.5 cm ginger, freshly grated
½ tsp sambal oelek
2 tbsp white wine vinegar
pepper
1 bunch coriander, freshly chopped
2 tbsp sesame oil

Preparation time: approx. 20 minutes (plus cooking time)
Per portion approx. 460 kcal/1932 kJ
18 g P, 8 g F, 75 g CH

Vegetable skewers
with feta

Serves 4

2 sprigs thyme

2 sprigs rosemary

1 bunch basil

350 ml olive oil

3–4 garlic cloves

2 onions

sea salt

pepper

500 g feta

2 small courgettes

1 small aubergine

1 green pepper

20 cherry tomatoes

250 g natural yoghurt

Preparation time: approx.
20 minutes (plus marinating and
grilling time)
Per portion approx.
308 kcal/1295 kJ
23 g P, 16 g F, 11 g CH

1 Soak wooden skewers in cold water. Wash the herbs, shake dry and pick off the leaves. Chop the thyme and rosemary finely and mix with 250 ml olive oil. Peel the garlic and onions. Crush the juice of 1 garlic clove into the mixture and season with salt and pepper.

2 Cut the feta into bite-size cubes. Trim and wash the courgettes, aubergine and pepper. Dice the courgettes and aubergine. Cut the pepper in half, remove the stalk end and seeds and cut the flesh in pieces. Cut the onions in four. Spear chunks of feta and vegetables on the skewers, alternating with washed cherry tomatoes. Leave to draw in the oil marinade for 20 minutes.

3 For the dip, purée the basil finely with the remaining olive oil. Mix in the yoghurt and season with salt and pepper.

4 Remove the skewers from the marinade and drain well. Grill on both sides for about 1–2 minutes. Serve hot with the dip.

Curry with chard and yoghurt

Serves 4

1 garlic clove

2 onions

3 green chillies

1 piece ginger (2 cm)

2 tomatoes

2 tbsp sunflower oil

½ tsp mustard seeds

1 pinch ground fenugreek
seeds

2 tbsp chilli flakes

10 curry leaves

½ tsp ground turmeric

sea salt

100 g fresh young red chard
leaves

300 g natural yoghurt

Preparation time: approx.
20 minutes (plus cooking time)
Per portion approx. 106 kcal/442 kJ
4 g P, 8 g F, 5 g CH

1 Peel the garlic clove and onions and chop finely. Trim and wash the green chillies, cut open and remove the seeds and white membranes. Peel the ginger and chop finely. Wash the tomatoes, remove the stalk ends and dice the flesh.

2 Heat the oil in a pan and fry the mustard seeds, stirring continuously. When they split open, add the garlic, fenugreek, chilli flakes and curry leaves and fry for 1 minute. Add the onions, whole green chillies and ginger and fry until the onions brown.

3 Mix in the tomatoes and turmeric and season with salt to taste. Wash the chard, drain and cut in strips. Add to the pan and fry for 5 minutes. Remove from the heat and slowly stir in the yoghurt. Warm up the curry and simmer for a further 3 minutes. Remove the curry leaves before serving.

Vegetarian main dishes

Tofu and broccoli stir-fry **with cashew nuts**

Serves 4

300 g broccoli
300 g tofu
3 stems lemon grass
120 g cashew nuts
4 tbsp groundnut oil
2 tbsp red curry paste
250 ml vegetable stock
5 tbsp lime juice
4 tbsp light soy sauce

Preparation time: approx.
30 minutes (plus cooking time)
Per portion approx.
364 kcal/1530 kJ
22 g P, 29 g F, 5 g CH

1 Wash and trim the broccoli, cut in florets and cook *al dente* in boiling salted water for approx. 8 minutes. Remove from the pan, rinse with cold water and leave to drain in a colander. Pat the tofu dry and cut in cubes of approx. 1 cm.

2 Wash the lemon grass and chop the white part finely. Toast the cashew nuts golden brown in a dry wok, stirring continuously. Remove from the wok, leave to cool and chop coarsely.

3 Heat the groundnut oil in the wok and fry the tofu cubes until golden brown. Remove the tofu and fry the lemon grass and curry paste in the remaining oil. Add the vegetable stock, broccoli and tofu and heat up. Flavour with lime juice and soy sauce, sprinkle with the cashews, and serve.

Spicy cauliflower

Serves 4

1 large cauliflower
sea salt
2 green, 2 yellow
    and 2 red peppers
4 shallots
4 garlic cloves
1 tbsp freshly grated ginger
2 tbsp garam masala
4 tbsp sieved tomatoes
1 tbsp chilli powder
3 tbsp groundnut oil
100 g natural yoghurt
3 tbsp single cream
6 tbsp pine nuts
chervil for garnishing

Preparation time: approx.
25 minutes (plus cooking time)
Per portion approx.
278 kcal/1166 kJ
11 g P, 17 g F, 13 g CH

1 Trim and wash the cauliflower, split into florets and blanch in lightly salted water for approx. 5 minutes. Then remove and leave to drain.

2 Wash and trim the peppers, cut in half lengthways, remove the seeds and dice. Peel the shallots and garlic and chop finely. In a bowl, mix all the vegetables apart from the cauliflower with the ginger, garam masala, tomatoes and chilli powder.

3 Heat the groundnut oil and fry the mixture lightly for approx. 6 minutes. Add the cauliflower florets and fry for approx. 3 minutes. Stir in the yoghurt and single cream.

4 Toast the pine nuts in dry pan, sprinkle over the cauliflower mixture and serve garnished with chervil.

Main dishes with
meat and poultry

Chicken stir-fry
with oyster mushrooms

Serves 4

500 g chicken breast
400 g sugar-snap peas
400 g carrots
150 g oyster mushrooms
3 tbsp sesame oil
200 ml vegetable stock
2 tbsp soy sauce
sea salt
pepper

Preparation time: approx.
20 minutes (plus cooking time)
Per portion approx.
270 kcal/1130 kJ
36 g P, 7 g F, 13 g CH

1 Wash the chicken breasts, pat dry and cut in strips. Trim the sugar snaps and remove any strings. Scrape the carrots and cut in slices. Trim the mushrooms, wipe with a damp cloth and cut in small pieces.

2 Heat the oil and brown the chicken strips well on all sides. Add the sugar snaps, carrots and mushrooms and fry for 2 minutes. Add the stock, cover and stew for about 8 minutes. Season with soy sauce, salt and pepper.

Stuffed kohlrabi

1 Soak the mushroom. Peel the kohlrabi bulbs and hollow out carefully. In a pan, heat the stock with the sugar, 1 tablespoon of sake, 1 tablespoon of soy sauce, the mirin and ½ teaspoon of salt, and cook the kohlrabi in it for about 15 minutes. Leave to cool in the stock. Then remove and reserve the stock.

2 Mix the chicken with the remaining salt, sake and soy sauce. Drain the mushroom and chop finely. Trim the spring onion and chop the white part.

3 Mix all the ingredients with the chicken and spoon into the kohlrabi. Steam over medium heat for about 20 minutes. Serve the stuffed kohlrabi with the beans and the stock.

Serves 4

1 dried shiitake mushroom
4 kohlrabi bulbs
600 ml dashi
1 tbsp sugar
2 tbsp sake
2 tbsp soy sauce
1 tsp mirin
1 tsp sea salt
150 g chopped chicken meat
1 spring onion
4 cm freshly chopped ginger
100 g steamed soya beans

Preparation time: approx.
30 minutes (plus cooking time)
Per portion approx. 100 kcal/420 kJ
18 g P, 2 g F, 5 g CH

Easy rice dish

with turkey breast

Serves 1

50 g rice (parboiled)
sea salt
150 g turkey breast fillet
1 onion
½ garlic clove
1 courgette
½ yellow pepper
2 tomatoes
1 tbsp groundnut oil
½ tsp curry powder
1 pinch ground ginger
100 ml vegetable stock
pepper

Preparation time: approx.
20 minutes (plus cooking time)
Per portion approx.
677 kcal/2843 kJ
51 g P, 27 g F, 57 g CH

1 Cook the rice following the instructions on the packet. Wash and dry the turkey meat and cut in strips. Peel and chop the onion and garlic. Trim and wash the vegetables, and dice.

2 Heat the oil and fry the meat for 2 minutes. Remove from the pan. Lightly fry the onion, garlic, curry and ginger; add the vegetables and fry for 2 minutes. Add the stock and simmer for 5 minutes.

3 Drain the rice and mix the rice and meat into the vegetables. Season with pepper.

134

Chicory rolls

1 Trim the chicory, remove the bitter heart, cut the heads in half, wrap in the cheese slices and place in an oiled ovenproof dish.

2 Peel the onion and chop finely, fillet the orange and dice the flesh. Dice the ham. Mix the onion with the yoghurt, white wine, diced orange and ham.

3 Wash, dry and chop the herbs. Flavour the yoghurt mixture with the spices and herbs and pour over the chicory. Sprinkle with the Parmesan. Bake in the oven at 190 °C (fan 170 °C, Gas Mark 3 ½) for about 15 minutes.

Serves 4

4 heads chicory
8 slices Limburger cheese
1 tbsp vegetable oil
1 onion
1 orange
80 g cooked ham
300 g natural yoghurt
4 tbsp white wine
½ bunch mixed herbs
sea salt, pepper
cayenne pepper, nutmeg
40 g freshly grated Parmesan
vegetable oil for greasing

Preparation time: approx.
15 minutes (plus cooking time)
Per portion approx. 230 kcal/962 kJ
21 g P, 11 g F, 9 g CH

Turkey schnitzel

on carrots and wild rice

Serves 4

800 g carrots

2 small onions

2 organic lemons

100 g basmati wild rice
mixture

4 turkey schnitzels
(each approx. 150 g)

1 tbsp olive oil

sea salt

pepper

Preparation time: approx.
30 minutes (plus cooking time)
Per portion approx.
430 kcal/1806 kJ
42 g P, 7 g F, 47 g CH

1 Wash and peel the carrots and cut in thin slices. Peel the onions and dice finely. Wash the lemons and wipe dry. Grate the peel with a lemon zester (or a fine grater). Squeeze one lemon and cut the other in segments.

2 Cook the rice in 200 ml boiling water with the lid on for approx. 20 minutes. Wash the meat, pat dry and fry in hot oil on each side for 2–3 minutes. Season with salt and pepper. Fry the lemon segments briefly in the pan. Remove the meat and lemon from the pan.

3 Lightly brown the onions and carrots in the oil in the pan for approx. 5 minutes. Add 100 ml water and the lemon juice and bring to the boil. Add the grated lemon rind. Season with salt and pepper. Place the schnitzels on top of the carrots and cook for 2–3 minutes. Garnish with lemon segments and serve with the rice.

Chicken breast
goujons on a bed of cucumber

Serves 4

450 g chicken breast
1 garlic clove
1 red chilli
2 tbsp vegetable oil
2 tbsp oyster sauce
1 tsp honey
1 tbsp rice wine
pepper
1 cucumber
½ bunch fresh mint

Preparation time: 20 minutes
(plus frying time)
Per portion approx. 146 kcal/513 kJ
25 g P, 3 g F, 2 g CH

1 Wash the meat, wipe dry and cut in strips. Peel and chop the garlic, Trim and wash the chilli, remove the seeds and cut in thin rings.

2 Heat the oil in a wok and stir-fry the goujons fiercely. Stir in the garlic, chilli, oyster sauce, honey and rice wine and fry for about 2 minutes more. Season with pepper.

3 Wash the mint, shake dry and cut the leaves in strips. Transfer the meat to a serving dish covered with slices of cucumber and garnish with strips of mint.

Beef fillet
Asian-style

Serves 4

500 g fillet of beef
½ tsp freshly ground black
  pepper
2 tbsp dark soy sauce
1 tbsp flour
6 dried tongku mushrooms
300 g oyster mushrooms
4 spring onions
1 fresh red chilli
4 garlic cloves
1 piece ginger (approx. 4 cm)
3 tbsp vegetable oil
4 tbsp oyster sauce
1 tbsp fish sauce
1 tsp honey
4 tbsp rice wine

Preparation time: approx.
30 minutes (plus marinating,
soaking and cooking time)
Per portion approx.
352 kcal/1477 kJ
30 g P, 23 g F, 8 g CH

1 Wash the beef, pat dry, remove the sinews and cut in cubes of approx. 1 cm. In a bowl, mix the meat with pepper, soy sauce and flour, cover and marinate for 1 hour in the refrigerator.

2 Meanwhile, wash the tongku mushrooms and soak in hot water for about 20 minutes. Trim the oyster mushrooms, wipe with a damp cloth and cut in chunks. Trim and wash the spring onions, cut in half lengthways and cut in pieces about 3 cm long. Trim and wash the chilli, cut in half lengthways and then in strips. Peel the garlic and ginger and chop finely.

3 Squeeze a little of the water out of the tongku mushrooms and cut in four. Heat the oil in a frying pan or a wok. Brown the garlic, ginger and meat fiercely for about 5 minutes over high heat, stirring continuously, then reduce the heat. Add both kinds of mushrooms, the spring onions, oyster sauce, fish sauce and honey, and cook for about 2 minutes over medium heat. Add the chilli strips and warm up, stir in the rice wine, and serve.

Saltimbocca alla romana

Serves 4

4 veal schnitzels (each 125 g)
4 large sage leaves
4 slices air-dried ham with
  no fat
2 tbsp vegetable oil
3 tbsp dry white wine
125 ml meat stock
sea salt
pepper

Preparation time: approx.
20 minutes (plus cooking time)
Per portion approx. 230 kcal/964 kJ
32 g P, 11 g F, 1 g CH

1 Beat the meat flat. Wash the sage leaves and shake dry. Top each slice of veal with 1 sage leaf and 1 slice of ham and fasten in place with toothpicks.

2 Heat the oil in a pan and fry the saltimbocca for 4 minutes on each side. Remove from the pan and keep warm.

3 Add the wine to the meat juices, add the stock and reduce the sauce by a third. Season to taste with salt and pepper. Pour the sauce over the saltimbocca and serve. A fresh green salad goes well with this.

Warm chick pea salad
with lamb

Serves 4

1 onion
1 garlic clove
1 small aubergine
400 g loin of lamb
5 tbsp olive oil
1 red pepper
4 spring onions
450 g chick peas (tinned)
6 sprigs lemon thyme
1 lime
2 tbsp white wine vinegar
½ tsp harissa paste or sambal
   oelek
sea salt
black pepper

Preparation time: approx.
35 minutes (plus cooking time)
Per portion approx.
490 kcal/2050 kJ
38 g P, 25 g F, 29 g CH

1 Chop the onion and garlic finely. Wash and trim the aubergine, cut in half lengthways and then in slices ½ cm thick.

2 Wash the lamb, pat dry and cut in strips 1 cm wide. Heat 2 tablespoons of olive oil in a pan and brown the meat on all sides. Then add the onions, garlic and aubergine and brown for about 2 minutes.

3 Meanwhile, wash, trim and dice the pepper. Wash and trim the spring onions and cut in wafer-thin rings. Rinse the chick peas in cold water and leave to drain.

4 Pick the leaves off the thyme, add to the meat, stir and transfer to a large salad bowl, along with the other salad ingredients. For the dressing, cut the lime in half, squeeze and beat the juice together with the vinegar, the remaining oil and the harissa paste. Season to taste with salt and pepper and pour over the salad.

Beef stir-fry
with spinach and mango

Serves 4

500 g lean beef
200 g leaf spinach
1 ripe mango
1 mild green chilli
3 tbsp vegetable oil
2 tbsp soy sauce
2 tbsp oyster sauce
2 tbsp sweet chilli sauce
½ bunch Thai basil

Preparation time: approx.
30 minutes (plus cooking time)
Per portion approx.
276 kcal/1157 kJ
28 g P, 16 g F, 5 g CH

1 Cut the meat in strips. Rinse the spinach well under running water, shake dry and cut in rough pieces. Peel the mango and cut the flesh in chunks. Wash the chilli and cut in rings. Wash the Thai basil and pick off the leaves.

2 Heat the oil in a wok and fry the spinach and chilli fiercely, then remove from the pan. Brown the strips of meat fiercely in the same oil. Add the soy sauce and oyster sauce and mix well.

3 Then add the mango to the meat. Lastly, return the spinach and chilli to the pan and mix with the meat. Flavour with sweet chilli sauce and sprinkle with Thai basil leaves before serving.

Szechuan beef

Serves 4

500 g lean beef
white of 1 egg
1 tsp cornflour
4 tbsp soy sauce
2 onions
2 garlic cloves
1 yellow and 1 green pepper
2 chillies
1 small leek
1 small aubergine
1 piece fresh ginger
  (approx. 3 cm)
1 tsp rice vinegar
2 tbsp rice wine
sea salt
pepper
vegetable oil

Preparation time: approx.
20 minutes (plus cooking time)
Per portion approx.
278 kcal/1165 kJ
29 g P, 11 g F, 12 g CH

1 Cut the beef in thin slices. Mix together the egg white, cornflour and 1 tablespoon of soy sauce and leave the beef in it to draw.

2 Peel the onions and garlic and cut the onions in thin rings. Trim and wash the peppers and chilli and chop finely. Trim and wash the leek and cut in thin strips. Trim, wash and dice the aubergine. Peel the ginger and chop finely.

3 Mix the remaining soy sauce with the rice vinegar and rice wine and set aside.

4 Heat the oil in a wok. Brown the beef over high heat, stirring continuously, then season with salt and pepper. Remove from the wok and set aside.

5 Heat a little oil, brown the aubergines, onions, ginger and the remaining vegetables, and crush the garlic into them. Stir-fry over high heat. Mix in the meat, add the sauce and mix well.

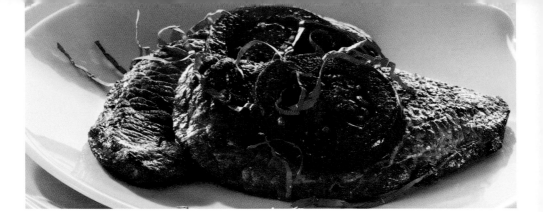

Veal schnitzel

with tomatoes

Serves 4

4 veal schnitzels
sea salt
pepper
3 tomatoes
4 tbsp olive oil
a few basil leaves

Preparation time: approx.
15 minutes (plus cooking time)
Per portion approx. 203 kcal/852 kJ
27 g P, 9 g F, 2 g CH

1 Wash the schnitzels, pat dry, beat flat and season with salt and pepper.

2 Wash the tomatoes, remove the stalk ends and cut in slices.

3 Heat the oil and fry the schnitzels on both sides for about 3 minutes.

4 Arrange the tomato slices on the schnitzels, cover and cook for a further 2 minutes. Season the tomatoes and garnish with strips of basil.

Ham and fruit stir-fry

1 Cut the ham in strips. Trim and wash the leek and cut in thin rings. Peel the pomelos and grapefruit, making sure you remove all the white pith. Then carefully cut out the segments.

2 Cut the figs in segments, wash and peel the kaffir lime and chop the peel finely. Wash the lime leaves and chop finely. Trim and wash the lemon grass and chop finely.

3 Heat the oil in a wok and brown the ham. After approx. 3 minutes add the pomelos, grapefruit, lime peel, lime leaves, figs and lemon grass. Flavour with the spices. After approx. 8 minutes transfer to individual bowls and serve garnished with slices of lime.

Serves 4

800 g smoked ham
1 leek
2 pomelos
2 pink grapefruit
2 figs
4 kaffir limes
2 kaffir lime leaves
1 stem lemon grass
3 tbsp groundnut oil
1 tsp each of powdered cardamom, anise, cloves and ginger
thin slices of lime for garnishing

Preparation time: approx. 30 minutes
Per portion approx. 349 kcal/1471 kJ
45 g P, 14 g F, 9 g CH

Main dishes with fish and seafood

Haddock

on a bed of carrots

Serves 4

1 untreated orange
400 g haddock fillets
black pepper
400 g carrots
1 tsp butter
1 tsp sugar
sea salt
4 tbsp vegetable stock
2 tbsp chive rings

Preparation time: approx.
30 minutes (plus cooking time)
Per portion approx. 175 kcal/733 kJ
20 g P, 5 g F, 11 g CH

1 Peel the orange with a zester. Fillet the orange, catching the juice and drizzling it over the haddock fillets. Sprinkle the fish with the orange peel and a little black pepper. Leave to draw for 10 minutes.

2 Peel the carrots and grate finely. In a pan, caramelise the butter and sugar, stirring continuously. Glaze the grated carrots in it, cover and cook for about 2 minutes.

3 Salt the carrots lightly and add the vegetable stock.

4 Season the fish and add the fish and the marinade to the carrots. Cover and cook for about 10 minutes.

5 Add the orange segments and warm up. Serve garnished with chive rings.

Grilled tuna
with wasabi and daikon

Serves 4

250 g sushi grade tuna
1 tsp black sesame seeds
2 tsp pink peppercorns
1 tbsp sunflower oil
16 shiso leaves
50 g daikon (Chinese mooli)
2 tsp wasabi

Preparation time: approx.
20 minutes (plus grilling and
cooling time)
Per portion approx. 180 kcal/756 kJ
14 g P, 13 g F, 1 g CH

1 Wash the tuna and pat dry. Place the fish in a shallow bowl.

2 Grind the sesame seeds and peppercorns coarsely in a mortar. Brush the fish with oil and toss in the ground spices.

3 Pre-heat the grill. Grill the tuna on a hot grill on both sides for about 30 seconds. Then return it to the bowl and freeze immediately for about 5 minutes.

4 Wash the shiso leaves and shake dry. Peel the daikon and grate finely. Cut the fish in slices 5 mm thick and serve with shiso leaves, wasabi and daikon.

Sea bass
in mustard cabbage

Serves 4

500 g sea bass
1 pak choi
1 tsp sea salt
1 tsp crushed black
 peppercorns
1 piece ginger (5 cm)
3 shallots
1 tbsp sunflower oil
2 tbsp sherry
6 tbsp vegetable stock
½ bunch coriander, chopped
½ bunch chives, chopped
1 tbsp sesame oil

Preparation time: approx.
30 minutes (plus cooking time)
Per portion approx.
460 kcal/1932 kJ
19 g P, 8 g F, 76 g CH

1 Wash the fish, pat dry and divide into 4 portions. Remove the largest leaves from the pak choi, trim and blanch briefly in boiling water. Drain and leave to cool. Place each fish fillet on the end of a leaf. Season with salt and pepper. Roll up the leaves, turning in the edges well.

2 Steam the fish parcels on a plate in a pressure cooker for 8 to 10 minutes, until the fish is cooked. Reserve the liquid and keep the fish parcels warm.

3 Peel the ginger and shallots and chop finely. Heat the oil in a pan and fry the ginger and shallots lightly. Add the sherry and boil away. Add the stock and steamer liquid and reduce a little. Mix in the chopped herbs and season to taste. Drizzle the fish parcels with sesame oil and serve with the sauce and a side dish of rice.

Asparagus and prawn stir-fry

Serves 4

6 dried shiitake mushrooms
250 g carrots
750 g green asparagus
sea salt
3 tbsp sesame oil
2 garlic cloves
1 red chilli
200 ml vegetable stock
3 tbsp oyster sauce
150 g peeled prawns
pepper

Preparation time: approx.
20 minutes (plus cooking time)
Per portion approx. 233 kcal/976 kJ
18 g P, 6 g F, 33 g CH

1 Soak the mushrooms in warm water for about 10 minutes. Meanwhile, scrape the carrots and cut in batons, peel the bottom third of the asparagus stems and cut diagonally in pieces.

2 Blanch the asparagus in boiling salted water for 5 minutes. Drain the mushrooms, remove the hard stalks and cut the caps in strips.

3 Heat the sesame oil in a wok. Peel and dice the garlic. Trim the chilli, remove the seeds and chop finely. Brown both lightly in the hot oil. Add the drained asparagus, mushrooms and carrot batons and stir-fry for 3 minutes.

4 Add the vegetable stock and oyster sauce and bring to the boil. Add the prawns and cook for 3 minutes. Season with salt and pepper. Serve with rice.

Mediterranean fish skewers

Serves 4

400 g cod back fillets
8 peeled giant scampi
1 courgettes
12 cherry tomatoes
1 garlic clove
3 tbsp olive oil
sea salt
pepper
1 tsp Italian herbs

Preparation time: approx.
20 minutes (plus cooking time)
Per portion approx. 236 kcal/991 kJ
38 g P, 7 g F, 3 g CH

1 Rinse the cod fillets in cold water, pat dry and cut in bite-size pieces. Rinse the scampi and pat dry.

2 Wash the courgettes, trim off the ends and cut in slices 1 cm thick. Wash the tomatoes and wipe dry.

3 Spear the prepared ingredients alternately on 8 skewers. Peel the garlic and chop finely. Mix together the garlic, oil, salt, pepper and Italian herbs, and brush the fish skewers with the mixture.

4 Pre-heat the oven grill to 250 °C (Gas Mark 9). Place the skewers on a baking sheet lined with foil and grill for about 8 minutes, turning the skewers occasionally and brushing thinly with the oil mixture.

Fish fillets
wrapped in courgettes

Serves 4

2 courgettes
sea salt
4 Nile perch fillets
pepper
3 tbsp lemon juice
3 tbsp olive oil
4 tbsp chopped oregano

Preparation time: approx.
35 minutes
Per portion approx. 218 kcal/915 kJ
218 g P, 5 g F, 3 g CH

1 Trim and wash the courgettes and cut lengthways in thin slices. In a pan bring lightly salted water to the boil and blanch the courgette slices in it for about 2 minutes. Drain, rinse in cold water and leave to drain in a colander.

2 Wash the fish fillets and pat dry. Cut each fillet in two, season with salt and pepper and drizzle with lemon juice.

3 Wrap the pieces of fish in the courgette slices and fasten each with a toothpick. Brush thinly with olive oil.

4 Pre-heat the grill and cover the grill rack with aluminium foil. Grill the fish parcels on each side for about 6 minutes. Alternatively you can use a grill pan.

Fish stir-fry
with celery and bean spouts

Serves 4

750 g assorted fish fillets,
   e.g. salmon, pike, zander,
   plaice, cod
1 lime
2 garlic cloves
½ stick celery
3 carrots
200 g soya bean sprouts
4 tbsp vegetable oil
1 tbsp honey
2 tbsp rice vinegar
sea salt
pepper
2 tbsp flour

Preparation time: approx.
30 minutes (plus cooking time)
Per portion approx.
292 kcal/1226 kJ
37 g P, 9 g F, 12 g CH

1 Wash the fish, pat dry, remove any remaining bones and cut in cubes. Squeeze the lime and drizzle the fish with the juice.

2 Peel the garlic and chop finely. Trim and wash the celery and cut in thin rings. Peel and dice the carrots. Wash the bean sprouts thoroughly and leave to drain in a sieve.

3 Heat 2 tablespoons of oil in a wok and lightly brown the garlic. Add the celery and carrots and stir-fry for 3 minutes. Then stir in the bean sprouts and warm up. Add the honey and vinegar. Remove the vegetables from the wok and keep warm.

4 Wipe out the wok and heat the remaining oil. Season the fish, toss in flour and fry in the hot oil until crisp. Remove from the wok, drain on kitchen roll and serve with the vegetables.

Sole

with lime sauce

Serves 4

2 sole, filleted and ready
   to cook
10 garlic cloves
5 red chillies
1 bunch chives
3 limes
1 tsp sea salt
3 tbsp light soy sauce

Preparation time: approx.
20 minutes (plus cooking time)
Per portion approx. 173 kcal/727 kJ
34 g P, 3 g F, 1 g CH

1 Wash the sole fillets and pat dry. Place in an ovenproof dish. Pre-heat the oven to 200 °C (Gas Mark 6).

2 Peel the garlic and slice thinly. Trim the chillies, wash inside and outside and cut in thin rings. Wash the chives, shake dry and chop coarsely. Squeeze the limes to produce approx. 5 tablespoons of juice.

3 In a bowl, thoroughly mix the chillies, garlic, lime juice, salt and soy sauce together with 125 ml water and pour over the fish. Bake on the middle shelf of the oven for approx. 20 minutes. Sprinkle with chives before serving.

Squid with coriander

1 Wash the squid, pat dry and cut in bite-size pieces. Trim and wash the spring onions, cut in half lengthways and then in pieces approx. 3 cm long.

2 Wash the coriander, shake dry and pick off the leaves. Peel the garlic and chop finely.

3 Heat the oil in a wok or a frying pan and fry the garlic for approx. 2 minutes until golden brown, stirring continuously. Add the squid and flavour with fish sauce, oyster sauce, coriander powder and pepper. Fry for approx. 2 minutes, then add the spring onions. Add approx. 50 ml water, mix well, season again to taste and mix in the coriander leaves shortly before serving.

Serves 4

700 g ready-to-cook squid
4 spring onions
4 sprigs coriander
4 garlic cloves
3 tbsp vegetable oil
2 tbsp fish sauce
2 tbsp oyster sauce
1 tsp coriander powder
2 tsp freshly ground white pepper

Preparation time: approx. 20 minutes (plus cooking time)
Per portion approx.
328 kcal/1375 kJ
29 g P, 4 g F, 26 g CH

Shellfish
with garlic and chilli

Serves 4

200 g mussels

400 g scallops

3 garlic cloves

2 red chillies

1 tbsp freshly chopped
   coriander root

1 tsp sea salt

2 tbsp vegetable oil

2 tbsp oyster sauce

1 tbsp nuoc mam
   (Vietnamese fish sauce)

1 green pepper

4 shallots

½ bunch mint

Preparation time: approx.
30 minutes (plus cooking time)
Per portion approx. 173 kcal/726 kJ
16 g P, 7 g F, 9 g CH

1 Brush the shellfish and discard any that are open. Cook in boiling water for 5 to 10 minutes until the shells open. Now discard any that are still closed. Remove the meat from the shells.

2 Peel and chop the garlic. Trim and wash the chillies, remove the seeds and chop. In a mortar, grind the garlic, chillies, coriander root and salt to a paste.

3 Heat the oil in a pan or a wok and briefly toast the paste, then add the shellfish. Stir in the sauces and cook for a few minutes more.

4 Trim and wash the pepper, remove the seeds and cut in thin strips. Peel the shallots and cut in rings. Wash the mint, shake dry and chop. Add the mint and vegetables to the shellfish and mix well. Fry for a further 3 minutes, then serve.

Main dishes with fish and seafood

Temaki sushi
with salmon and prawns

Makes 20 sushi of each kind

For the sushi rice:
400 g sushi rice
1 nori sheet
5 tbsp Japanese rice wine
7 tbsp rice vinegar
4 tbsp sugar
1–2 tbsp mirin
1–2 tbsp salt or soy sauce

1 Tip the rice into a sieve and rinse until the water remains clear. Then leave to rest in the sieve for approx. 12 minutes.

2 Put the nori sheet in a pan, cover with 100 ml water and leave to soak for 5 minutes. Then add 600 ml water, the rice wine and the rice. Cover, bring to the boil and leave to simmer until all the water is absorbed and the rice is cooked. Then allow all the moisture to evaporate from the rice and remove the nori sheet.

3 Mix together the rice vinegar, sugar and mirin with salt or soy sauce until the sugar and salt have dissolved and stir into the rice while it is still warm. Keep stirring the rice until it has completely cooled. Then form the rice into balls the size of a table-tennis ball and cover with a damp cloth to prevent them from drying out.

4 For the sushi, in a pan, briefly toast the 10 nori sheets on one side. Then lay them on a worktop and cut in half. For each one, cut approx. 3 cm from a half-sheet of nori, place a ball of rice on top and smooth flat.

5 Spread the rice with a little wasabi paste and top with a lettuce leaf, letting it extend a bit over the top edge.

6 Cut the salmon in thin strips approx. 5 cm long; cut the feta cheese in small cubes. Wash and dry the chives and cut in pieces.

7 Wash the prawns and pat dry. Cut the omelette in small cubes and mix with the prawns. Add cucumber strips to complete the filling.

8 Spread the desired filling and garnish on the rice. The filling should protrude a little at the upper edge. Roll up to form a small, pointed cone with the filling peeping out. Fasten the end of the nori sheet in place with a few grains of rice.

For the sushi:
10 nori sheets
Wasabi paste or wasabi powder
    mixed with water
20 decorative lettuce leaves,
    not loo large and without
    hard ribs

For the salmon filling:
200 g smoked salmon
50 g feta cheese
½ bunch chives

For the prawn filling:
200 g North Sea prawns
50 g omelette
cucumber strips

Preparation time: approx. 20 minutes
Per portion approx. 529 kcal/2212 kJ
32 g P, 10 g F, 78 g CH

Main dishes with fish and seafood   173

Desserts and sweets
for slimming

Exotic fruit salad

Serves 4

200 g lychees (tinned)
1 star fruit
4 figs
100 g kumquats
1 mango
4 kiwis
1 baby pineapple
2 tbsp coconut milk
unsweetened pineapple juice
  if desired
50 g grated coconut for
  sprinkling

Preparation time: approx.
20 minutes
Per portion approx. 223 kcal/932 kJ
2 g P, 9 g F, 31 g CH

1 Drain the lychees in a sieve and catch the juice. Wash and dry the star fruit and cut in thin slices. Wash the figs, remove the hard stalks and cut in eight. Wash and dry the kumquats and cut in thin slices. Wash and dry the mango, cut in half, remove the stone, peel and dice the flesh.

2 Peel and dice the kiwis, peel the baby pineapple and cut in bite-size pieces. Mix the fruits together in a bowl. Mix the lychee juice with coconut milk and pour over the fruit. If necessary, add pineapple juice as well. Sprinkle with grated coconut and serve.

Grape compote
with limes

Wash and dry the grapes, cut in half and remove the seeds. Squeeze the limes and top up the juice with water to give 200 ml. Bring the grapes and lime juice to the boil with the cinnamon and simmer over low heat for about 2 minutes.

Add the concentrated fruit juice, chop the cashew nuts and mix in. Leave to cool before serving.

Serves 4

600 g green grapes
3 limes
2 tsp cinnamon
5 tbsp concentrated fruit juice
2 tbsp cashew nuts

Preparation time: approx.
20 minutes
Per portion approx. 216 kcal/910 kJ
2 g P, 5 g F, 32 g CH

Creamy berry sorbet

Serves 4

1.5 kg mixed frozen berries
8 tbsp blossom honey
8 tbsp lime juice
80 ml freshly squeezed orange
 juice
fresh berries for decoration

Preparation time: approx. 10 minutes
(plus freezing time)
Per portion approx. 217 kcal/1137 kJ
4 g P, 1 g F, 52 g CH

1 Purée all the ingredients in a blender to give a creamy mixture. Transfer to a bowl and freeze, stirring occasionally with a fork.

2 Pick over the fresh berries, wash and pat dry.

3 Spoon the sorbet into 4 individual bowls, decorate with the fresh berries and serve immediately.

Wholegrain crêpes
with fruit purée

1 Make the sifted flour, 2 tablespoons of honey, salt, walnut oil, coconut flakes, eggs, 125 ml water and the milk into a smooth batter and leave to rest for 30 minutes.

2 Wash the apricots, remove the stones and cut in small pieces. Wash the pears, cut in half, remove the stalks and cores and cut the flesh in small pieces. Purée the fruit in a blender. Mix the fruit purée with the yoghurt and the remaining honey.

3 Heat the oil in a pan and fry 6–8 thin pancakes, drain on kitchen roll and pile on a plate. Cut 1 pancake in strips.

4 For each pancake, put 1–2 tablespoons of fruit purée in the middle, fold the edges to the middle and tie at the top with a strip of pancake to look like a sack.

Serves 4

125 g wholegrain wheat flour
3 tbsp honey
1 pinch salt
1 tbsp walnut oil
1 tbsp coconut flakes
3 eggs
125 ml milk
150 g apricots
150 g pears
1 tbsp natural yoghurt
2 tbsp sunflower oil

Preparation time: approx.
40 minutes (plus resting and cooking time)
Per portion approx. 183 kcal/769 kJ
6 g P, 7 g F, 24 g CH

Cold rose hip soup
with grape juice

Serves 4

250 g dried rose hips

unsweetened grape juice for topping up

4 tbsp maple syrup

7 g vegetable thickener

1 tbsp honey

juice of ½ lemon

2 tbsp whipped cream

Preparation time: approx. 20 minutes (plus soaking, cooking and cooling time)
Per portion approx. 53 kcal/225 kJ
1 g P, 1 g F, 12 g CH

1 Crush the dried rose hips in a mortar and soak in water for about 4 hours. Then simmer in the same water for about 30 minutes.

2 Strain the soup through a sieve and top up the liquid with grape juice to 1.5 litres. Add the maple syrup and bring to the boil. Mix the thickener with a little cold water, then add to the boiling rose hip mixture to thicken it.

3 Leave the soup to cool. Flavour with 1 table-spoon of honey and the lemon juice. Top each plate of soup with a dollop of whipped cream.

Plum salad **with ginger**

1 Wash and trim the plums and blanch in boiling water for approx. 6 minutes. Drain and leave to cool. Skin the plums, cut in half and remove the stones. Cut the preserved ginger in thin strips and mix with the plums.

2 Mix the single cream with the plum juice, cinnamon and powdered ginger. Put the fruit in a bowl with the sauce and leave to draw for 30 minutes. Sprinkle with freshly grated ginger, and serve.

Serves 4

500 g plums
2 pieces preserved ginger
4 tbsp single cream
20 ml unsweetened plum juice
1 pinch cinnamon
1 pinch powdered ginger
freshly grated ginger for serving

Preparation time: approx. 30 minutes (plus time to cook, cool and draw)
Per portion approx. 97 kcal/407 kJ
1 g P, 2 g F, 17 g CH

Quark with dried fruit

Serves 4

200 g dried fruit, e.g. plums
  and apricots
400 ml freshly squeezed
  orange juice
500 g low-fat quark
4 tbsp ground almonds

Preparation time: approx.
15 minutes (plus soaking time)
Per portion approx. 209 kcal/877 kJ
19 g P, 4 g F, 38 g CH

1 Soak the dried fruit in the orange juice for about 1 hour. Then remove the fruit from the juice and cut in small cubes.

2 Mix the quark with the juice, fold in the remaining ingredients and serve.

Pineapple stuffed with raspberries and blackberries

1 Wash the baby pineapples and cut in half lengthways, leaving the peel and leaves on, remove the hard inner core, scoop out some of the flesh and cut in small chunks.

2 Pick over the raspberries and blackberries, wash and pat dry. Slice the bananas, mix with the berries and drizzle with the lime juice.

3 Mix the yoghurt with the coconut syrup. Stuff the pineapple halves with the fruit. Arrange on plates and pour over the coconut yoghurt. Sprinkle with cinnamon and grated coconut and serve.

Serves 4

2 baby pineapples
100 g raspberries
100 g blackberries
2 small bananas (not fully ripe)
juice of ½ lime
200 g natural yoghurt
30 ml coconut syrup
cinnamon and grated coconut
  for sprinkling

Preparation time: approx. 25 minutes
Per portion approx. 128 kcal/539 kJ
3 g P, 2 g F, 27 g CH

Melon with vinaigrette

Serves 4

1 small cantaloupe melon

½ cucumber

3 tomatoes

crystal salt

3 tbsp freshly chopped mint
 leaves

3 tbsp olive oil

2 tbsp white balsamic vinegar

½ tsp ground cumin

mint leaves for garnishing

Preparation time: approx.
20 minutes (plus time to draw)
Per portion approx. 64 kcal/269 kJ
1 g P, 4 g F, 5 g CH

1 Cut the melons in half, remove the seeds and scoop out the flesh with a melon baller. Trim, peel and dice the cucumber. Wash the tomatoes, cut a cross in the skins, remove the stalk ends, plunge the tomatoes in boiling water, remove the skins and seeds, and dice.

2 In a bowl, mix the melon balls, cucumber and tomatoes with salt and 2 tablespoons of chopped mint. Leave to draw for 10 minutes.

3 Make a vinaigrette with the oil and vinegar, the remaining mint, cumin and salt, and drizzle over the salad. Leave to draw for a further 30 minutes. Serve garnished with mint.

Strawberry salad
with nectarines

Serves 4

250 g strawberries
2 nectarines
1 untreated orange
4 tbsp maple syrup
40 g pine nuts
150 g natural yoghurt

Preparation time: approx.
20 minutes (plus marinating time)
Per portion approx. 180 kcal/750 kJ
5 g P, 7 g F, 23 g CH

1 Wash the strawberries briefly and leave to drain well. Reserve 4 nice strawberries for decoration. Remove the green parts from the remaining strawberries with a sharp-pointed knife and cut the berries in half lengthways.

2 Wash the nectarines and wipe dry. Remove the stones and dice the flesh.

3 Wash the orange in hot water and dry. Grate the peel finely and squeeze out the juice. Whisk the peel and juice with 2 tablespoons of maple syrup and drizzle over the strawberries and nectarines. Cover and marinate in the refrigerator for about 1 hour.

4 Toast the pine nuts in a dry, nonstick pan until golden brown. Reserve 1 tablespoon and purée the remainder with the yoghurt. Flavour with the remaining maple syrup.

5 Pour the pine nut sauce over the strawberry and nectarine salad. Arrange the reserved strawberries in the middle and sprinkle with the remaining pine nuts.

Citrus granita
with blossom honey

1 Wash and dry all the fruits and cut very fine strips of the peel.

2 Squeeze the fruits and strain the juice.

3 Bring the mineral water and honey to the boil and allow to cool again.

4 Mix the fruit juice, the finely chopped peel and the chopped lemon balm with the honey syrup and freeze in a bowl.

5 Stir several times with a fork. Transfer to plates and serve immediately.

Serves 4

1 untreated orange
1 untreated grapefruit
1 untreated lime
1 untreated lemon
200 ml mineral water
50 g blossom honey
4 leaves lemon balm

Preparation time: approx. 15 minutes (plus cooling and freezing time)
Per portion: approx. 76 kcal/316 kJ
1 g P, 0 g F, 17 g CH

Chilled yoghurt soup
with berries

Serves 4

250 g natural yoghurt

100 ml organic blackberry
  juice

20 mint leaves

400 g berries (e.g. blueberries
  or blackberries)

mint leaves for garnishing

Preparation time: approx.
15 minutes (plus cooling time)
Per portion approx. 88 kcal/326 kJ
3 g P, 1 g F, 14 g CH

1 Mix the yoghurt thoroughly with the blackberry juice and pour into a bowl. Wash the
mint leaves, pat dry and cut in strips. Stir into the
yoghurt and refrigerate for approx. 30 minutes.

2 Pick over the berries, wash, pat dry and
remove any stalks. Then chill briefly in the
freezer compartment. Fold into the yoghurt and
serve in individual portions decorated with a few
mint leaves.

Chilled cherry soup
with hazelnuts

1 Mix the kefir well with the honey, cinnamon and nuts. Cool thoroughly.

2 Put the cherries and raisins into 4 soup bowls.

3 Pour over the kefir and chill well before serving.

Serves 4

1 litre kefir
50 g blossom honey
1 tsp ground cinnamon
50 g chopped hazelnuts
200 g stoned sour cherries from a jar.
2 tbsp raisins

Preparation time: approx. 5 minutes
Per portion approx. 305 kcal/1274 kJ
11 g P, 12 g F, 31 g CH

Index

Picture credits

Fotolia.com: pp. 8/9 (© Warren Goldswain), 10 (© Yuri Arcurs), 11 (© Hannes Eichinger), 12 (© contrastwerkstatt), 13 (© Francesco83), 14 (© Subbotina Anna), 15 (© silencefoto), 16 (© Africa Studio), 19 (© Mara Zemgaliete), 20 (© eyewave), 21 (© Printemps), 22 (© Barbara Dudzinska), 24 (© Kaarsten), 25 top (© Ildi), 25 bottom (© oksix), 26/27 (© HLPhoto), 28 (© rolfbrecht100), 29 (© BestPhotoStudio), 32 (© Christian Schwier), 33 (© Jonas Glaubitz), 34 (© Konstantin Yuganov), 35 (© Dionisvera)

Recipe photos pp. 4, 52/53, 77, 79, 85, 91, 96, 104–108, 112, 126, 136, 140, 147, 148, 151, 168/169, 173: Studio Klaus Arras

All other photos: TLC Fotostudio